Table of Contents

Eureka: The Solver Owner's Handbook

Introduction

Welcome to the world of streamlined problem solving. Eureka: The Solver is an equation solver with a difference; this program solves systems of equations (linear, nonlinear, and transcendental), and it also:

- Solves high-order polynomials
- Evaluates derivatives and definite integrals
- Minimizes and maximizes functions with or without constraints

Eureka makes it easy for you to solve your real-world mathematical problems very quickly, without having to first learn numerical approximation techniques.

You don't have to be a computer specialist to use Eureka. It was designed for people like you—scientists, engineers, financial analysts, and all other professionals and students—people who need to solve equations and who would rather use a computer instead of a calculator to do the solving.

What Can You Do With Eureka?

Eureka is a versatile tool designed for solving any problem that can be expressed as a system of linear or nonlinear equations. Its capabilities range from solving the simple to the very complex.

Without any special training, you can use Eureka to solve:

- Simple linear equations in one variable
- Systems of linear equations
- Nonlinear equations or systems of equations
- Maximizations or minimizations of a variable
- High-order polynomials (real and complex)
- Derivatives and definite integrals

Eureka also:

- Works with inequalities
- Plots and prints the graphs of functions
- Converts units automatically
- Generates reports

Eureka contains several built-in functions, including:

- The familiar trigonometric functions
- The logarithmic and exponential functions
- Several useful statistical and financial functions

The program also includes a Calculator Mode, which has all the features of a powerful hand-held calculator, that can also access Eureka's built-in functions.

Eureka is very easy to work with. You don't need programming knowledge or experience to use it. You simply type in an equation file containing the equation(s) to be solved, then use the Solve command to solve for the variables in your equations. The equations you enter use standard mathematical representations, very similar to those you enter in a calculator when solving the same problems the hard way.

If you get stuck while in Eureka, you can ask the program for on-screen help by simply pressing a key.

The Eureka text editor, which you use to enter the equation file, is virtually identical to Borland's SideKick and Turbo Pascal editors. If you are familiar with one of these editors, Eureka's editor will be no problem for you. Or, if you have ever used WordStar or a WordStar-like editor, you are already familiar with the editing syntax and commands. For those who do not have experience with a similar ASCII text editor, we have included several useful tables, a tutorial, and an appendix covering the Eureka editor.

Eureka displays solutions on the screen in their own windows, along with information about how confident it is that the solution is correct.

After Eureka solves the equation file, you can plot graphs of the functions in the file by simply specifying the function and the range you want plotted. Eureka will display a graph of the function, with the coordinate axes scaled appropriately. You can also print out the equation file, the solutions, and the graphs in the form of a written report.

Structure of This Manual

This chapter, "Introduction," tells you the basics about Eureka: what you can use the program for, how to use the manual, and what hardware and software you need to run the program.

Chapter 1, "Overview," gives an overall picture of the different parts of Eureka and how they fit together. Experienced software users can probably read this chapter and get started right away with Eureka.

Chapter 2, "Getting Started," shows you how to load Eureka, then gives a progressive tutorial designed to familiarize you with using the editor, creating and solving problems, and incorporating some special techniques into your files.

Chapter 3, "Modeling Tips and Techniques," summarizes the tasks that Eureka performs, describes the program's advanced features, and gives some tips on modeling.

Chapter 4, "Menu Commands and Settings," describes each of the commands in the main menu and the submenus, and explains the settings that you can change with the Settings command.

Chapter 5, "The Equation File: Syntax, Directives, and Functions" describes what you put into an equation file, shows you how to formulate the entries, tells what directives are and shows how to use them in the file, introduces Eureka's built-in functions, provides detailed explanations of the built-in financial functions, and explains what user-defined functions are and how to write them.

Chapter 6, "Worked Examples," is a collection of solved equation files taken from typical scientific, engineering, and financial problems.

Appendix A, "Quick Reference Table," briefly explains many of Eureka's functions.

Appendix B, "Eureka Editor Commands," summarizes the Eureka editor commands.

Appendix C, "Built-in Functions," describes Eureka's built-in functions.

Appendix D, "A DOS Primer," contains basic information about DOS, with a focus on creating and using directories.

Appendix E, "Error Messages," lists all Eureka error messages and their meanings.

Appendix F, "Customizing Eureka," tells you how to use the EINST program to custom-install Eureka.

The Glossary gives definitions of key terms used in this manual.

The Index lists page references for program features, commands, and windows.

Typography

The body of this manual is set in this typeface — Roman. Special typefaces are used for the following purposes:

Alternate Type	This typeface is used to show something as it appears on the screen or to show anything you must type.
< >	Angle brackets indicate data that depends on your system and should not be typed verbatim.
Italics	Italics are used to introduce a new term; all new terms are defined in the Glossary.

Mathematical expressions are set in Roman type according to standard textbook notation except when they represent what you actually type into a Eureka equation file; these are set in alternate type, and some mathematical operators appear differently. For instance, the multiplier symbol, $\times$, is replaced with * in alternate type, exponents (e.g. x^2) are represented by a caret (x^2), and $\leq$ and $\geq$ are represented by < = and > = .

The Distribution Disk

The Eureka distribution disk contains:

- EUREKA.EXE, the program itself.
- PROB1 through PROB12, sample equation files.
- README, a message you should read before loading Eureka.
- README.COM, a program to assist you in reading README.
- EINST.COM, a program to customize Eureka keystrokes, set a path to your files, set the default edit mode, and set the screen mode.
- EUREKA.MAC, SuperKey macros for mathematical symbols (SuperKey is a keyboard enhancer program from Borland International).

- HELP.EKA, Eureka's on-line help text.
- NDP.COM, a program that determines if an 8087 math coprocessor chip is present in your computer.
- Sample equation files corresponding to the worked problems in Chapter 6 (various file names ending in .EKA.)

The file README contains important information about using Eureka. Before loading and using EUREKA.EXE, you should look over the README file.

Hardware and Software Requirements

Eureka runs on the IBM PC family of computers, including the XT and AT, along with most IBM compatibles.

Eureka requires:

- DOS 2.0 or higher
- At least 384K of RAM

Eureka will run on any 80-column monitor. A math co-processor chip (an 8087) significantly enhances performance, but is not required. Eureka will display plots in graphics mode if you have a CGA, EGA, or Hercules graphics card but a graphics card is not required.

The Eureka program is in a file called EUREKA.EXE. It is not copy-protected, so you can easily transfer it to a hard disk or RAM disk. However, you should read Borland's No-Nonsense License Agreement at the front of this manual for an explanation of your responsibilities with respect to copying Eureka, and then sign it and mail to us .

Acknowledgements

In this manual, references are made to several products:

- SideKick, Turbo Basic, and Turbo Pascal are trademarks of Borland International, Inc.
- WordStar is a trademark of MicroPro, Inc.
- IBM PC, XT, and AT are trademarks of International Business Machines, Inc.

Eureka: The Solver Owner's Handbook

Overview

This chapter takes a brief look at Eureka: The Solver. If you are an experienced software user, this chapter may be all you need to get going with Eureka. Check Appendix A, "Quick Reference Table," for more information.

If you are new to computers and software, you'll probably want to read this chapter and then turn to Chapter 2 for the step-by-step tutorials.

This chapter summarizes the four typical steps that you and Eureka go through to solve a problem, and explains features of each step:

- Edit (create an equation file for a problem)
- Solve (find a solution)
- Verify (verify the solution's accuracy)
- Report (print the results)

All Eureka problems begin with the preparation of an equation file using the Eureka editor. Chapter 5 details the contents, syntax, and format of an equation file. Chapter 2 gives tutorials designed to familiarize you with preparing an equation file.

Command Menus and Windows

Eureka uses pull-down command menus and windows. If you have not used pull-down menus before, you will find the following few comments helpful.

The main menu runs across the top of the screen. When the menu is active, there is always one highlighted item. You can select an item by moving to it with the arrow keys, then pressing *Enter*, or simply press the key corresponding to the first letter in the item. For instance, to select Solve, you can simply press *S*. Each time you select a menu item, Eureka either opens up a new menu or executes a command.

If the main menu is not active, it is because some window or submenu is active.

Generally, when a window is active, all keyboard actions affect only that window. In most cases, you can move around in the windows with the cursor keys. The most important windows are:

- Edit
- Progress
- Solution
- Verify
- Plot
- List
- Report
- Help
- Error message

These windows are fully described in Chapters 2 and 4. The following keys affect windows:

Esc	Either closes the active window or moves it to the background, making another window or menu active.
Arrow Keys	With *Scroll-Lock* on, move windows. With *Scroll-Lock* on and *Shift* or *Num-Lock* on, resize windows.
F1	Calls up a Help window that gives context-sensitive help. Wherever you are in Eureka, you can press *F1* and a help message appears on the screen.

The Editor

Eureka features an ASCII editor for editing problem files. You can create and modify problem files with this editor while in Eureka, or with the ASCII editor of your choice. The command syntax of the Eureka editor is described in Chapter 4.

To call up the editor and create a new file, select Edit from the main menu or select New from the File menu.

To call up the editor and modify an existing file, select the File menu from the main menu, select Load, and specify an existing equation file name. When you press *Enter*, Eureka brings the named file into the Edit window.

To save a file for later modification or examination, select Save from the File menu.

Equation File Syntax

An equation file consists of a collection of formulas, typically one per line, written in standard mathematical notation. Eureka recognizes the following symbols:

Relational operators	$= \; < \; >$
Arithmetic operators	$+ \; - \; * \; / \; \char94 \; (\;)$
Functions	exp, ln, sin, cos, abs

as well as variable names, numerical constants, and some special operators, functions, and directives. The caret symbol (^) is the exponentiation operator, as in

$$x\char94 2 = x * x \text{ or } 5\char94 3 = 5 * 5 * 5 = 125$$

Variables

A variable name may be any sequence of letters, digits, and periods, starting with a letter. Uppercase and lowercase are distinguished in variable names, but not in built-in functions or file names.

Initializations

If you know an approximate solution in advance, we recommend that you enter the approximate values as initializations. The notation

```
x := 12.75
```

means that Eureka should initially assign the value 12.75 to the variable x. Eureka will use its own default initialization $(x := 1)$ if you give no value.

More information on the equation file syntax can be found in Chapter 5.

Special Symbols

The symbols that follow have special meanings within the Eureka program. The symbols and their meanings are listed, along with reference to where you can find a detailed explanation of each.

Symbol	Where to Find an Explanation
:=	Initialization or user-defined function, Chapter 5
$	Directives, Chapters 4 and 5
#	Commands/Calculator, Chapter 4
;	Comments, Chapter 5
{}	Comments, Chapter 5

Reserved Words

Eureka's reserved words call up built-in functions. Look in Chapter 5 for directives, and in Appendix C for most built-in functions. Refer to Chapter 5 for definitions of the financial functions, marked here with F. Directives are marked here with a dollar sign ($).

Eureka Reserved Words		
abs	im	pos
$ accuracy	$ include	F pval
atan2	$ initval	$ radius
$ casefold	integ	re
$ complex	$ listdefault	$ rootsign
cos	ln	$ settings
cosh	log10	sgn
$ digits	$ max	sin
deriv	$ maxtime	sinh
$ end	$ min	$ solve
exp	ncum	sqrt
fact	F paymt	$ substlevel
$ finanmode	$ penalty	sum
$ finansmooth	pi	$ syntax
floor	$ plotdefault	tan
frac	polar	tanh
F fval	poly	$ units

Solving Equations

After preparing the equation file, you select Solve from the main menu. Eureka solves the problem and displays the solutions to the equation file's functions and equations in the Solution window.

How Eureka Calculates Solutions

When Eureka solves a problem, it searches for a solution and then displays resultant values for all of the relevant variables in the Solution window. If there are too many variables to fit into the window, you can scroll through the Solution window with *PgUp* and *PgDn*.

To determine the accuracy of a minimization or maximization solution, Eureka computes a confidence level between 0 and 100. This is a rough indicator of how well Eureka has performed. 100 is perfect. A confidence level between 93 and 100 means that Eureka successfully found a solution.

In some cases a solution may not exist or may not be unique. Read Chapters 3 and 5 for techniques that will help you avoid giving such problems to Eureka.

Evaluating Equations

You use Verify from the Commands menu to evaluate expressions in the equation file, using data from the Solution window. Use Verify to verify the accuracy of a previously computed result.

When you select Verify, Eureka evaluates all expressions in the equation file. The program ignores directives and initializations, solves no equations, and changes no variable values. Eureka displays the results of the evaluation in the Verify window.

When an equation or inequality appears in the equation file, Eureka evaluates the left- and right-hand sides using data from the Solution window, then calculates the difference between the two sides of the equation (or inequality). If the difference indicates that the equation or inequality is invalid, the program gives an error message.

Reporting

When you need a hard copy of the solution and the equation file, select Report from the main menu. From the Report menu, select the output device and appropriate format, then select Go. The report contains a copy of the equation file, the Solution window information, the last plot or table graphed, and the Verify window information.

Getting Started

This chapter helps you get going with Eureka: The Solver through a progressive tutorial. It also contains tables that summarize Eureka's main menu, special function keys, and the editor commands.

If you are a novice personal computer user or are unfamiliar with menu-driven software, we recommend that you take a few minutes to sit down at your computer with this manual and follow through the tutorial. When you complete it, you will know:

- How to load (and leave) Eureka
- How to create, solve, modify, and print out a problem
- How to work with some of the program's special features

In the tutorial, you will first set up (load) the program so you can use it when and how you want. Then you will read the text and follow the instructions given in the tutorial, which gives you hands-on experience with using Eureka to solve a real problem.

The tutorial first introduces you to Eureka's menus and text editor, takes you step-by-step through creating and solving a problem, then shows you how to implement some of Eureka's special features.

Note: Any time you need help while in Eureka, just press *F1* to bring up context-sensitive help screens.

Setting Up the Program

Before you begin working with Eureka, you should make a copy of the distribution disk. Use the copy as your working disk, and store the original in a safe place in case anything should happen to the copy.

You don't need to know much about your computer to use Eureka: All you need to know is:

- How to turn the system on
- How to handle and *format* a floppy disk
- How to start DOS

Appendix D, "A DOS Primer," contains useful information about DOS.

Copying to a Floppy Disk

One Floppy Disk Drive

To copy the files from the distribution disk to another floppy disk using a system with one disk drive:

1. Insert your DOS disk in the disk drive. Type

    `DISKCOPY` *Enter*

    Your system will respond with

    `Insert Source diskette in Drive A and press Enter when ready`

2. Take the DOS disk out of the disk drive and insert the Eureka disk, then press *Enter*.

    After reading the contents of the Eureka disk into memory, your system will prompt you to

    `Insert Target diskette into Drive A and press any key when ready`

3. Insert a blank, formatted floppy disk into the drive and press any key. When your system finishes copying the contents of the Eureka disk from memory to the new disk, it will ask if you want to

    `Copy another?`

    Type

    `N` *Enter*

Two Floppy Disk Drives

To copy the files from the Eureka disk to another floppy disk using a system with two disk drives:

1. Insert the Eureka disk in Drive A and a blank, formatted disk in Drive B.

2. Type

   `COPY A:*.* B:` *Enter*

Copying to a Hard Disk

To copy the files from the distribution disk to a hard disk:

1. Insert the Eureka disk in Drive A. If you use directories, note the full *path name* of the *directory* in which you want the program to reside.

2. Type

   `COPY A:*.* C:<full path name>` *Enter*

   (assuming your hard disk is Drive C).

Copying to a RAM Disk

If your system has a RAM disk, you can use it to speed up the program's access time. This means you must copy the Eureka program to the RAM disk each and every time you boot the computer, unless you use an AUTOEXEC.BAT file. (See the next paragraph for how to modify the AUTOEXEC.BAT file.) Type

`COPY A:EUREKA.EXE D:` *Enter*

(assuming that your RAM disk is on Drive D) each time you want to load Eureka.

If you already have an AUTOEXEC.BAT file, you can automate this process by putting a reference to EUREKA.EXE in the AUTOEXEC.BAT file. For instance, assuming your hard disk is Drive C,

1. Use your word processor to bring the AUTOEXEC.BAT file to the screen. (It should be in the root directory.)

2. Find the line that copies programs from their home directories to Drive D.

3. Add

```
C:<full path name>\EUREKA.EXE
```

to this line. For example, if EUREKA.EXE is in a directory called
EUREKA, the line will look like this:

```
COPY C:\EUREKA\EUREKA.EXE D:
```

4. Save the updated AUTOEXEC.BAT file.

You can also create an AUTOEXEC.BAT file if you don't already have one. For
more information, see Appendix D.

Tutorial Part 1: Using the Menus and the Editor

This first part of the tutorial explains how to use Eureka's menus and submenus,
and how to create and save a file. It tells you how to:

- Start Eureka
- Understand Eureka's program screens
- Write a new file
- Save the file

Starting Eureka

Eureka requires no installation. Once the program is in your computer (either on a
floppy disk in the disk drive, or on your hard disk), all you need to do is call it up.

For a floppy-disk system, make sure your working disk (the floppy disk with the
copied version of Eureka on it) is in the desired drive (typically Drive A, which we
will refer to in this manual).

Then to start the program, *log on* to the drive or directory that contains the
working disk and type

```
EUREKA Enter
```

After a few moments, the Eureka opening screen appears (Figure 2-1).

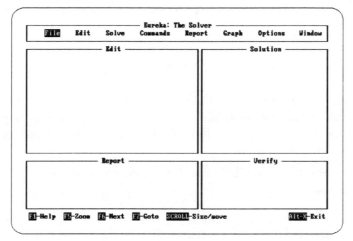

Figure 2-1   Opening Screen

What to Do If You Want Out of Eureka

Before you begin pressing keys on the keyboard and getting into Eureka, it's a good idea to know how to get out.

The Escape (*Esc*) key always returns you to Eureka's previous active state. Since you are starting at the opening screen, pressing *Esc* from within one of Eureka's program screens will eventually bring you back to the opening screen. The main menu bar is always visible; you can't escape past it (unless you exit the program by pressing *F Q*.)

As Figure 2-1 shows, the opening screen is made up of two features: the *main menu* and the *status line*.Once the opening screen appears, you can use any Eureka feature: select an item from the main menu and then make a selection from a submenu.

Look over the screen on your display and compare it to Figure 2-1. Note that the main menu remains on the screen virtually all the time you use Eureka; so does the status line. What appears on the status line varies from time to time; this is explained later.

A menu presents a list of options from which you can choose. When you select an item from the main menu, that item's pull-down menu extends from the main menu. Each pull-down menu contains a group of related functions. The File menu, for instance, lists operations concerned with files — making them, saving them, and so on.

The status line lists keys that perform special functions in Eureka. For instance,

- *F1* displays a window of context-sensitive help text.
- *F5* "zooms" the active window to fill the screen.

Different keys are active under different circumstances, so the keys displayed on the status line change from time to time. You'll see this in the tutorials and in the worked examples in Chapter 6.

Table 2-1 summarizes Eureka's main menu options, and Table 2-2 lists the special function keys.

Table 2-1 Main Menu Summary

Entry	Option	Description
FILE	Load	Bring an existing file to the screen
	New	Open a new file for editing
	Save	Write the current file to disk
	Write to..	Save the current file under the file name you specify
	Directory	List files in the specified directory
	Change dir	Change the active drive/directory
	Rename	Rename a file
	OS shell	Temporarily exit to DOS
	Quit	Leave Eureka and return to DOS
EDIT		Create a new file or modify an existing file
SOLVE		Find the value of the specified variable(s)
COMMANDS	Verify	Evaluate both sides of the equation and compare the result
	Calculator	Open a window in which arithmetic functions can be solved
	Find other	Search another area for the value of the specified variable
	Iterate	Continue iterating the value of the specified variable
REPORT	Go	Print/save a report about an equation file
	Output	Specify output device
	Formatted	Put report into formatted form
	Capture	Log your work to a file on disk
	Log file name	Specify name for capture file
GRAPH	Plot	Plot a graph of a user-defined function
	Output	Specify output device
	List	Generate a table of values for a user-defined function
	Function	Enter function to allow plotting or graphing
OPTIONS	Variables	Change value of variable(s) or constants
	Settings	Open a submenu of user-modifiable settings
	Colors	Change window colors
	Directories	Specify where Eureka looks for its files
	Load setup	Let a predefined group of settings be used
	Write setup	Save a group of settings as a file
WINDOWS	Open	Open the specified window
	Close	Close the active window
	Next	Open and make active the next window
	Zoom	Expand the active window to fill the screen
	Tile	Make all open windows visible and of equal size
	Stack	Stack open windows at largest possible size
	Goto	Go to the active window

Table 2-2 *Summary of Special Function Keys*

Function Keys	Description
F1	Display help text
F2	Save current file
F3	In editor, open new file
F5	Zoom active window
Alt-F5	Text zoom for plot (graph) window
F6	Change active window
F7	Go to active window (in editor, Block begin)
F8	In editor, Block end
Alt-X	Exit Eureka
Alt-E	Go to Edit window
Alt-S	Solve the equation file
Alt-C	Activate the calculator
Alt-P	Insert pi character
Esc	Return to previous activity
Ctrl-Break	Interrupt a solve
Arrow keys and PgUp, PgDn	Move/scroll through screen
Scroll-Lock, Num-Lock, and arrow keys	Resize window
Scroll-Lock and arrow keys	Move window to new position

Making a Selection From the Main Menu

There are two ways to select a menu item: the cursor method and the initial letter method.

- *The cursor method*: Move to the right or left with the *Right arrow* and *Left arrow* keys. When the item you are interested in is highlighted, press *Enter* to open a pull-down menu containing details about that item. Use the *Up arrow* and *Down arrow* keys to move the highlight bar up and down in the menu; press *Enter* to select an item from the menu.

- *The initial letter method*: Press the key for the first letter of the item. For instance, to select File, press *F* (lowercase or uppercase); the File pull-down menu will appear (Figure 2-2). To select Save from the File menu, press *S*.

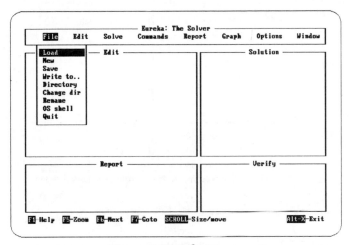

Figure 2-2   File Menu

Creating a File

Although Eureka allows you to use any ASCII text editor you like, we will use the one supplied with the program to write a sample file.

To create a file, you need to start at the main menu. Select New by pressing *F N*. Figure 2-3 shows the Edit window as it should appear after you have entered some text into the file.

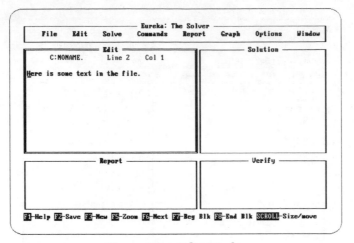

Figure 2-3   Edit Window

You can think of a window as a place where things happen—where you interact directly with the program.

- Some windows display a prompt, requesting more information;
- Others display the results of a particular operation;
- Still others, such as the Edit window, let you enter data or text.

Using the Eureka Editor

Notice the information at the top of the window on your screen:

- "C:NONAME" displays the active drive and the file's name.
- "Line 1" and "Col 1" refer to the position of the cursor; it is on the first line, in the first space or column.
- "Insert" tells you the editor is in Insert mode, not Overwrite typing mode.
- "Indent" shows that automatic line indention is available.

To write something into your new file, you type text just as you would if you were using a typewriter, remembering to press *Enter* at the end of every line. (Eureka's editor has no word-wrap feature.) Then, to move the cursor around in the text, you can use the cursor keys on the numeric keypad or the *PgUp* and *PgDn* keys.

Table 2-3 summarizes selected editor commands you may find useful while working through the tutorials. The editor is discussed in greater detail at the end of this chapter and in Appendix B.

Table 2-3 *Summary of Editor Commands*

To Move the Cursor

One space right	*Ctrl-D* or *Right arrow*
To first letter of word on right	*Ctrl-F* or *Ctrl-Right arrow*
To right end of line	*Ctrl-Q D* or *End*
One space left	*Ctrl-S* or *Left arrow*
To first letter of word on left	*Ctrl- A* or *Ctrl-Left arrow*
To left end of line	*Ctrl-Q S* or *Home*
One line up, same column	*Ctrl-E* or *Up arrow*
One screen up, same column	*Ctrl-R* or *PgUp*
To top of present screen	*Ctrl-Home*
Beginning of file	*Ctrl-Q R*
One line down, same column	*Ctrl-X* or *Down arrow*
One screen down, same column	*Ctrl-C* or *PgDn*
To bottom of present screen	*Ctrl-End*
To end of file	*Ctrl-Q C*

To Delete Text

One character, where cursor rests	*Ctrl-G* or *Del*
One character, immediately left of cursor	*Backspace*
Whole word, immediately right of cursor	*Ctrl-T*
Whole line, where cursor rests	*Ctrl-Y*

To Insert Text

In between existing text	*Ctrl-V* or *Ins* (toggle Insert ON)
Write over (replace) existing text	*Ctrl-V* or *Ins* (toggle Insert OFF, Overwrite ON)

Now that you understand how to use the Eureka Editor, write something in your file. For example, you could type

```
I'm learning how to use Eureka, and      Enter
soon my problem-solving problems will     Enter
be over.                                  Enter
```

Saving A File

With some text in your file (although it doesn't contain any equations yet), this is a good time to save it and then continue working: Select Save from the File menu. When prompted, enter TRIAL as the name for your file.

A Eureka file name follows standard DOS conventions: one to eight characters with an optional one-to-three-letter extension. In a file name, you can use any letters or numbers, and the symbol __.

You can use either uppercase or lowercase letters in the file name; when it comes to file names, Eureka is not case sensitive. (That means that Eureka doesn't know the difference between uppercase and lowercase letters; for example, the file names TEST, test, and Test all look the same to Eureka.)

Although the file doesn't disappear from the screen, a copy of it has been saved to disk, under the name TRIAL. To bring this saved file to the screen, you would use the Load command on the File menu.

Tutorial Part 2: Creating and Solving an Equation File

This part of the tutorial demonstrates how to use Eureka to solve a real problem and print a report. It tells you how to:

- Create a problem file
- Solve the problem
- Modify the equation file to contain a user-defined function
- Plot the graph of the function
- Print a report about the problem

The first step is to write an equation file. When you create an equation file, you assemble the various parts of a problem in a way that Eureka understands. An equation file contains one or more equations and any initializations, directives, functions, and comments that are required.

You will write an equation file that contains an equation and a comment. You will then solve it, modify it to contain a user-defined function, and plot a graph of that function.

Creating the Equation File

To write the equation file, ask Eureka to load in the file named TRIAL; type

F L

Eureka will ask you the

Load file name

Enter the name of the file you created earlier:

TRIAL *Enter*

A window appears containing the file you previously saved. However, you can only look at the file from this window; you can't make any changes to what you see because you are not yet in the Edit window. To edit the file, select the Edit option from the main menu: press **E**.

In the next step, you will create a typical equation file containing an equation and a comment.

Writing an Equation

You write equations, one per line, in standard mathematical syntax and notation, with a few special symbols. For now, all you need to know about equation syntax is that:

- The exponentiation operator is the caret symbol, ^. For instance, x to the third power is written as x^3.
- Multiplication is not performed implicitly.
- Multiplication is denoted with an asterisk, * (3 times z is written as 3 * z).

(For more information about equation file syntax, refer to Chapter 5.)

The equation you will solve resembles a polynomial; it may or may not have three roots. After solving for the first root, you will use some special techniques to determine if there are other roots.

Enter the following equation to be solved:

```
x^3 + 3 * x^2 - 2 * x - cos(x) = 0
```

Double check that you have typed the equation correctly. If you make a mistake, use the editor commands given in Table 2-3 to correct it.

Writing a Comment

Comments must either be set off by a semicolon (;) or appear between braces ({ }).

To enter a comment, press **Enter** (to skip a line, improving legibility), then type

```
{ Test of equation solving }
```

You can set off the comment with a semicolon instead:

```
; Test of equation solving
```

The text you entered into the file during the first part of the tutorial can also be converted to a comment. Eureka can't solve the equation file if you just leave the text as is, so if you don't want to set it off as a comment, delete it. To erase or delete lines of text, see the editor commands in Table 2-3.

When the file contains only comments (appropriately set off) and the equation, return to the main menu and select Solve. Eureka will first look directly, then iteratively, for an answer to the problem. While Eureka searches for an answer, a Progress window appears on the screen. It displays the amount of time the program is using to find the solution, the current amount of error, and the current solution.

As Eureka iterates, it modifies the current variable values, then checks to see if the modified values yield the desired function value. The current amount of error is a measure of the difference between the desired function value and the function value calculated by using the current variable values.

When the program finds a solution, the Progress window disappears and the Solution window (Figure 2-4) takes its place.

The Solution window displays the values Eureka has found for the indicated variables. For the equation file TRIAL, Eureka determines x to be equal to 0.77442927.

The Progress window is useful if you want to interrupt a lengthy solving process. To interrupt a Solve and examine the current variable values:

- Press *Ctrl-Break*
- Examine the current solution
- Resume solving by selecting Iterate from the Commands menu

Notice that the keys listed on the status line change as soon as the Solution window appears. The new keys affect only the currently active window.

To move the cursor in the Solution window ("scroll the window"), use the arrow and *PgUp* and *PgDn* keys (just as in the Edit window).

After the Solution window appears, you can still tell Eureka to continue looking for solutions by selecting Iterate from the Commands menu.

Often the solution process is so quick that you do not see the Progress window. For minimization and maximization problems, after you select Solve, you will see interim iterative solutions in the Progress window.

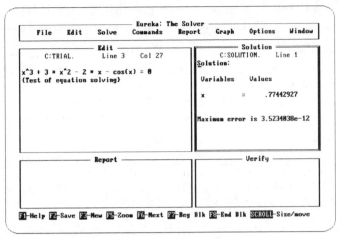

Figure 2-4   *Solution Window*

Modifying the Equation File

You have determined one root of the equation to be 0.77442927. But what about the other roots this equation may have?

You need to examine a graph of the equation to see if the other roots exist. The Eureka plotting feature allows you to graph the equation and determine if there are other values of x for which the function $f(x) = 0$.

If you try to use either the plotting or table (list) feature now, you will find they are inactive; verify this by pressing **Esc** then **G** to select the Graph menu.

Look closely at the Graph menu. Plot, Output, and List are dim, meaning that you cannot use them yet. You can only access the Function option; Plot, Output, and List are unavailable because they have no user-defined function to work with.

In order for you to use Plot (or List), an equation file must

- include at least one user-defined function and
- have been solved

or else you must enter a user-defined function directly into the program using the Function option. Let's modify the file to incorporate a user-defined function and then solve it.

First get back into the Edit window by pressing *F6* until the Edit window is active (indicated by double bars around it). Then press *F7* to go to the window. Use the editing commands listed in Table 2-3 to change your equation file so it looks like this:

```
f(x) := x^3 + 3 * x^2 - 2 * x - cos(x)
f(x) = 0

{ Test of equation solving }
```

(The symbol $:=$ indicates that $f(x)$ is a user-defined function.)

Return to the main menu screen, then solve the problem again by pressing *Esc*, then *S*.

Once you've verified that the solution is the same ($x = 0.77442927$), continue on to the next step and plot the function.

Plotting a Graph

Re-select the Graph option from the main menu by pressing *G*. All the options are now available because the equation file contains a user-defined function. (None of the options are dim, and you can move the highlight bar up and down throughout the whole menu.)

Select the Plot option by pressing *P*. Now set the left and right endpoints of the plot's horizontal (x) axis; when the Left endpoint prompt appears, type -4 *Enter*; when the Right endpoint prompt appears, type 4 *Enter*.

(If you hadn't responded to these prompts, Eureka would have plugged in the default values for Plot (-2 and 10), and would have plotted and displayed a different section of the function.)

Since Eureka automatically scales the vertical (y) axis, a graph of the function appears immediately (Figure 2-5). Notice that several different sized point-like characters have been used to draw the plot. This has the effect of smoothing out the curve: If one type of character were used exclusively, the plot would appear to be much more jagged.

If you have a graphics card in your computer, you can press the Zoom key (*F5*) to see the plot in graphics mode.

To see a larger-scale version of the plot, with scaled axes, press *Alt-F5* (To then return to the smaller version, press *Alt-F5* again.)

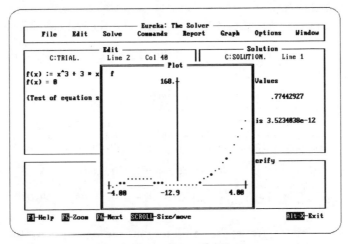

Figure 2-5 *First Plot Screen*

This plot shows that there are at least two roots to the equation. One root is close to −4. A region from about −1.5 to 1.5 may contain two roots, the 0.77442927 value already solved for, as well as a third root.

To examine this region more closely, select the Plot option again, but this time use −4 and 1 as the left and right endpoints. This generates the plot shown in Figure 2-6.

This second graph shows what the two roots must be. In the next part of this tutorial, after printing a report, you will select Variables from the Options pull-down menu to solve for the other two roots more exactly.

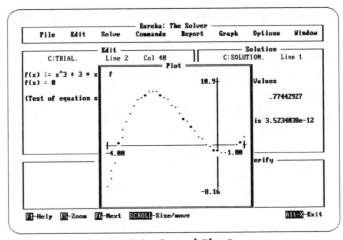

Figure 2-6 *Second Plot Screen*

Printing a Report

Now you will print a report that includes the original equation file with the latest solution and plot.

Select Report from the main menu. The Report menu offers several ways to store or print an equation file:

Output   lets you send the report to one of three places: to a file for saving, or to the printer or the screen for printing.

Formatted   lets you specify a left margin and page breaks.

Use the arrow keys to select Output and then press *Enter* to display a menu of the output choices.

To select the printer, press *P.* To select a formatted report, move the cursor to Formatted and toggle to *yes* with *Enter.* To print the report, use the *Up arrow* key to highlight *Go* and then press *Enter.* This sends the formatted report to your printer.

Tutorial Part 3: Using Special Features

This part of the tutorial gives instructions for using some of Eureka's special features on the equation file. This tutorial tells you how to:

- Use the editor to add to the equation file, write a directive, and tailor settings to fit the current equation file
- Change default settings
- Select the Variables option and find other roots
- Evaluate the equation
- Save the equation file
- Use the Window menu to manipulate windows
- Leave the program

Writing a Directive

Now you will add a directive to the equation file TRIAL. A *directive* is a command that overrides the defaults for various conditions.

For instance, although the default for solved variables is eight digits, you can use the *digits* directive to cause Eureka to display up to 13 digits (the internal limit).

All directives follow the general format of the example directive shown in this tutorial. To find out more about directives, refer to Chapter 5.

To change the number of displayed digits from eight (the default value) to ten, for example, add the following line to your equation file:

```
$ digits = 10
```

Changing Default Settings

This is a good time to change additional settings. Most of the settings that you can change with a directive can also be changed directly on the screen, using the main menu Options command.

In general, you change the settings by entering a number or by pressing **Enter** to toggle between *yes* and *no*. Specific conditions that apply to the individual settings are described on page 72 and in Chapter 5 under Directives.

The accuracy setting is an example of one you can change with a directive or with the Settings command. Accuracy affects Eureka's iterative solution searches by defining how much a solution is subject to its attendant constraints.

A *constraint* is a condition that a solution must meet in order to be valid. For instance, in our equation file TRIAL,

$$f(x) = 0$$

is a constraint.

Eureka will solve for x iteratively, and the smaller the accuracy setting is, the closer Eureka will try to make the left-hand side to the right-hand side of the equation.

(The penalty setting also affects the relative importance of the constraints in an equation file; see the description of penalty on page 93.)

To change the accuracy setting in TRIAL, first select Options from the main menu, then select Settings from the Options pull-down menu. Next, select Accuracy setting: Highlight *Accuracy* and press *Enter*. Then type

```
1.0e-10    Enter
```

This new setting replaces the default value of $1.0e-7$. This smaller number increases the accuracy of the solution when Eureka resolves any constraints that may exist in the equation file.

Now select Solve from the main menu. Eureka will solve the modified equation file TRIAL, taking into account the directive to display ten decimal places and the new, tighter accuracy requirement. The Solution window should read

```
x = .7744292653
```

Selecting the Variables Option and Finding Other Roots

With Variables from the Options menu, you can restart Eureka's search for a solution to TRIAL, starting at a value you specify. This is helpful if you have found a local minimum or maximum and want Eureka to search other regions.

Select the Variables option: press *Esc O V*.

The variables window lists the current solution for x as 0.7744292653. To start Eureka searching for a root in a different region of the x axis, you must enter a new value for the variable x. The new value must be close to the value you believe the alternate root to be.

When you plotted the equation file, you saw that there is another root to the equation very close to -4. To find the root that lies just above -4, type *Enter* -4 *Enter*, then press *Esc Esc C* to activate the Commands menu and select Find other. This second solution should be

```
x = -3.620186934
```

You can solve for the third root by repeating the substitution procedure just described, using a value for x close to -1. The third solution should be

```
x = -0.3288122319
```

Evaluating the Solution

You can use Verify to check the validity of any one of the solutions. This command evaluates each side of the solved equation individually and then compares the two sides; the difference between the two results should ideally be 0.

Eureka may find an unwanted or inappropriate solution (such as a negative root, when the value you need must be greater than zero). With the Verify command, you can identify such solutions. Knowing which solutions do not apply, you can modify the file so that Eureka finds the appropriate solutions.

To use Verify, press **Esc**, then type **C V** to select Verify from the Commands menu. The Verify window appears (Figure 2-7). The Verify command does not find a new solution; rather, it evaluates each side of the already-solved equation, then compares and displays the results.

Notice that the left-hand side of the equation has been evaluated to be a very small number, which results in an error of the same amount. (You may need to move the cursor down to display the amount of difference.) In this case, the amount of error is minuscule, so you can disregard it.

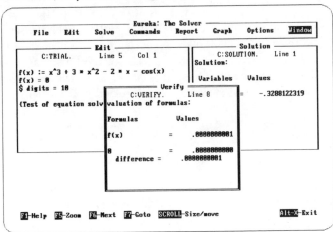

Figure 2-7   Verify Window

Using the Window Menu

The Window menu allows you to manipulate Eureka's windows. You can open, close, rearrange, and move back and forth between windows by selecting items on this menu.

Open and Close do exactly what they say: Open opens and makes active the window you specify, and Close closes the active window and removes it from the screen. Next is also easy to use; it moves from window to window, making each window active in turn. (The function key *F6* does exactly the same thing.)

Goto simply moves to the active window.

The other items on the Window menu — Zoom, Tile, and Stack — allow you to enlarge, shrink, and rearrange your windows.

Let's play around a little with the four windows that are currently on screen: Edit, Solution, Plot, and Verify. Suppose you'd like the Plot window to be larger. Press *F6* until the Plot window is active. Press the *Scroll-Lock* and *Num-Lock* keys. Now press the *Up arrow* key until the window is as big as you want it, then press *Esc*. If you just want a window to be as big as the entire screen, select Zoom and the window will expand to fill the screen. (The function key *F5*, the Zoom key, does the same thing.) To "dezoom" the window, press *F5* again.

Now let's move the Verify window to a different spot on the screen. Press *F6* until the Verify window is active, then press the *Scroll-Lock* key. Use the four arrow keys to push the window around the screen.

Finally, you can arrange all the windows at once. Select Tile, and all the windows will line up neatly side by side in a tile-like pattern, each the same size. Now select Stack. All the windows will pile atop each other in a neat stack in the center of the screen. When windows are either stacked or tiled, you can move from one window to the other by pressing *F6* as usual. When windows are stacked, press *F6* to "shuffle" them until the window you are interested in is on top.

Saving the Equation File

This marks the end of the tutorial. If you want to experiment with the equation file TRIAL (perhaps change other settings, or add directives, or print a report containing all three solutions), you should save it now.

To save the file, press *Esc* to return to the main menu, then type *F S* to select Save from the File menu.

Leaving the Program

Finally, to leave the Eureka program, select Quit from the main menu to return to DOS, or press *Alt-X*.

Wrap Up

This tutorial has introduced basic features of Eureka:

- You have learned how to create, edit, solve, and save an equation file; how to move between and manipulate windows; and how to return to DOS.

- You have learned that the usual sequence of operations is to write a problem, set options, solve the problem, and then evaluate the solution.

- You have learned how to produce both a graph and a written report.

But these are just basics; you will find that Chapter 3 describes useful special features, and Chapter 6 offers several worked examples. The example files can also be found on the Eureka disk. In addition, there are twelve other example files on disk under the file names PROB1 through PROB12.

(**Note**: PROB10 is an example that demonstrates the use of special IBM characters. If you have the APL character ROM installed, you will not be able to use this example.)

You might want to experiment with these files since they illustrate some of Eureka's important mathematical capabilities, such as maximizations and minimizations, not shown in the tutorial. In addition, a close reading of Chapters 4, 5, and 6 will show you how to fine-tune your equation file.

When you feel fairly proficient with the program, you may want to try running some problems in batch mode. See page 42 for information.

Eureka Editor Summary

This section explains some of the editor's basic features, and gives some tips about using the editor. For descriptions of all the editor commands, refer to Appendix B. To change any of Eureka's default editor keystrokes, use the EINST program (described in Appendix F).

Eureka's editor is an ASCII text editor. It does not introduce non-ASCII characters into the file being worked on. For this reason, files created with Eureka are compatible with other programs.

General Editing Techniques

If you have used a word processing program before, using the editor to create and modify a Eureka file will be very simple.

If you have never used a word processing program, Eureka's text editor will be easy for you to learn. One purpose of the tutorials in this chapter is to give you some practice with Eureka's editor before you dig in and start solving problems.

Basically, you use Eureka's editor like you do a typewriter, except that what you type appears in the Edit window rather than on a piece of paper.

When you want to move the cursor to a new location in your file, you use Control commands.

- *Ctrl-C* means to hold down *Ctrl* on your keyboard while you press *C*.
- *Ctrl-Home* means to hold down *Ctrl* on your keyboard while you press *Home*.

The Eureka editor works very much like the Turbo Pascal editor or like Word-Star in non-document mode, using many of the same Control commands.

Basic Features of the Editor

Two typing modes
The editor has two typing modes: *Insert* and *Overwrite*. In Insert mode, anything you type is inserted at the cursor position. In Overwrite mode, pressing a key replaces the current character at the cursor position with the new typed character. By default, the editor operates in Insert mode (you can change the default with the EINST program; see Appendix F). To switch modes, press *Ins* or *Ctrl-V*.

No word-wrap
Unlike a more standard word processing program, the editor does not have word-wrap. You must press *Enter* at the end of every line.

Autoindent
The editor has an autoindent feature that allows subsequent lines to automatically indent. If you leave several spaces at the start of a line, use *Ctrl-O I* to indent subsequent lines the same amount. This command sequence is a toggle, so you only need to press *Ctrl-O I* again to stop indenting.

The F5 ZOOM key
Sometimes you may want to see more than the area covered by the current Eureka window. You can "zoom" the screen, temporarily blanking out all windows and menus by pressing *F5*. Zooming the Edit window converts the entire screen into an editor environment. To return to the previous screen, with all windows and menus intact, press *F5* again.

Editing ASCII files

In addition to the equation file, you can edit files created by another ASCII editor, the report files Eureka generates, and any setup files you create.

Scroll-Lock and the F6 key

To move the Edit window, you must first activate the window by pressing *F6*. To move the window, press *Scroll-Lock* then use the cursor arrow keys. When the Edit window is in its new position, reactivate the window by again pressing *Scroll-Lock*.

More About the Editor Commands

Cursor movement commands control the position of the cursor in the file. You can edit your file by using only the cursor keys, *PgUp* and *PgDn*; the rest of the commands listed here are handy but not critical for small files.

Word left   *Ctrl-Left arrow* or *Ctrl-A*
Moves the cursor to the beginning of the word to the left.

Word right   *Ctrl-Right arrow* or *Ctrl-F*
Moves the cursor to the beginning of the word to the right.

Insert and delete commands let you insert and delete text and control the typing mode.

Delete character to left   *Backspace*
This is the "backspace" key immediately above the *Enter* key. It moves one character to the left and deletes the character there.

Delete character under cursor   *Del* or *Ctrl-G*
Deletes the character under the cursor and moves any characters that are to the right of the cursor over one position to the left. This command does not work across line breaks.

Delete word right   *Ctrl-T*
Deletes the word to the right of the cursor. This command works across line breaks.

Delete line   *Ctrl-Y*
Deletes the line containing the cursor and moves any lines below one line up.

Insert mode on/off   *Ins* or *Ctrl-V*
This command lets you toggle between Insert mode (the default) and Overwrite mode while entering text. In Insert mode, new text is tucked in at the cursor position and existing text is moved over to the right. In Overwrite mode, new characters replace existing characters as you type over them.

Modeling Tips and Techniques

This chapter covers some of the techniques you can use with Eureka to solve problems. It also discusses Eureka's problem-solving method. The last section gives some tips for successful modeling.

The techniques covered include:

- maximizing and minimizing
- continuing a search
- modifying constants and variables
- finding alternate solutions
- running problems from batch files
- interface with data files (sample BASIC input file)

How Eureka Works

This section discusses the inner workings of Eureka, covering both the program's strengths in solving many types of difficult problems and its limitations with regard to the phrasing of equations.

For examples of the solutions Eureka finds for real problems, refer to Chapter 6. For more information about error messages, turn to Appendix E.

After reading in an equation file, Eureka sorts out the relevant variables and formulas. It then performs symbolic manipulations and substitutions to eliminate any extraneous variables. If the problem cannot be solved directly, Eureka recasts it as a minimization problem.

Eureka minimizes functions by the steepest-descent method. This method involves starting at some initial point, and proceeding along a path which is always in the direction of the most rapid decrease for the function.

If there are constraints, the solution path goes from the initial point to the constraint manifold, and then lies on the constraint manifold until Eureka finds a solution.

Mathematically speaking, the solution process is actually more complicated than this description suggests. The manifold of points has a Riemannian metric which is derived from the Hessian of the function being minimized. The constraints are enforced by adding a penalty function.

Many problems have multiple solutions. Eureka's search method finds one at a time. The program can find other solutions if you insert different starting values or if you add constraints that exclude undesirable solutions. You can also use the Find other command, which directs Eureka to sample distant points in hopes of finding another promising search region.

There is no known efficient algorithm that always yields the solutions to all problems. Eureka does its best, but its solution path will occasionally get trapped in a region far from the actual solution.

Because some variables are eliminated before the search begins, it is not necessary to initialize them. Only the active variables influence the search process.

Solving Techniques

This section covers the various solving techniques you can use with Eureka.

Maximizing and Minimizing

In addition to solving equations, Eureka can solve maximization and minimization problems. This means that, instead of just finding any values for the variables which satisfy the given constraints, Eureka can find values for the variables which satisfy the constraints, and maximize or minimize some variable among all possible values of the variables which satisfy the constraints.

Maximization or minimization is thus an additional requirement imposed upon a set of equations or inequalities. You impose this requirement by inserting either the *max* or *min* directive in the equation file. *Max* and *min* work on variables, not on functions; if you need to maximize or minimize a function, you first need to define a variable equal to the function, then direct Eureka to *max*(or *min*)imize the variable.

For instance, suppose you want to find the maximum value of a profit function, where the relationships between the variables are expressed by

```
Profit(x,y) := 4 * x + 2 * x * y - 3 * y + 10
```

Before Eureka can maximize this relationship, you need to add the proviso that

```
P = Profit(x,y)
```

Then the program can follow the directive

```
$ max(P)
```

Continuing a Search

If Eureka is unable to solve a set of equations directly, it uses an iterative method. With the iterative method, the program obtains better and better approximations until a solution satisfies certain preprogrammed convergence criteria. If you think Eureka gave up too soon on a given problem, you can select Iterate from the Commands menu, and the program will continue to look for solutions.

You can interrupt a search by pressing **Ctrl-Break**. Eureka will then give the current values of the variables as the solution.

Modifying Constants and Variables

Sometimes Eureka finds a solution other than the intended one, or gets off the track looking for a solution. Usually this is due to an inadequate initialization. It is possible to restart the iterative procedure with new initial values by using the Variables command on the Options menu.

When you select the Variables command, a window opens showing the equation file variables and constants that can be modified. You select one with the cursor keys, then type in a new value to replace the current value.

Finding Alternate Solutions

Many systems of equations have several distinct solutions. Normally, Eureka is satisfied when it finds one solution. To find other solutions, select Find other from the Commands menu. This causes Eureka to try to find a solution different from the one already obtained. You can use the Find other command repeatedly to find multiple solutions.

You can also use the Find other command to find other local minima to a minimization problem or to find other local maxima to a maximization problem.

Running Problems from Batch Files

In solving a large number of problems, it may be more convenient to run them directly from DOS or from a batch file rather than from the Eureka pull-down menus. The syntax for doing this is

```
>Eureka ProblemFile OutputFile
```

where

```
>
```

is the DOS prompt, and

```
ProblemFile
```

is the problem file name.

```
OutputFile
```

is the output file to be created.

The output is the same as an unformatted Eureka report.

Some interactive capabilities, such as plotting, are not available when you run Eureka from DOS.

Because Eureka uses standard ASCII files, it can take input from a wide variety of ASCII programs.

For example, suppose you are working in Borland's Turbo Basic, and have twenty points in an *x-y* plane. These are stored in arrays $X(I)$ and $Y(I)$, where I runs from 1 to 20, the $X(I)$ are the points' *x*-coordinates, and the $Y(I)$ are the respective *y*-coordinates.

The following Turbo Basic program will create a file called PROBLEM and write the data on that file in a format suitable for Eureka to solve:

```
cls
defdbl a-z
dim X(20), Y(20)
A = 5
B = 1.2
for i = 1 to 20
 X(i) = i/10 - 1
 Y(i) = A * exp(-B * X(i)^2) + 0.001 * rnd
next i
open "O", 1, "PROBLEM"
print #1, "$ substlevel = 0"
print #1, "F(X) := A * exp(-B * X^2)"
print #1, "A := 4"
print #1, "B := 1"
for i = 1 to 20
 print #1, "F("; X(i); ") = "; Y(i)
next i
close #1
```

This Turbo Basic program will create the following Eureka equation file:

```
$ substlevel = 0
F(X) := A * exp(-B * X^2)
A := 4
B := 1
F(-.9 ) = 1.892596768501327
F(-.8 ) = 2.319901816869821
F(-.7 ) = 2.777704759459417
         .
         .
         .
```

Refer to Chapter 6, Problem 6, for an example problem in which this technique can be quite useful.

Modeling Tips for Successful Problem-Solving

This section provides some tips on how to set up problems in ways that Eureka can handle well.

Helping Eureka Find Correct Solutions

Sometimes Eureka does not find the correct solution or gives an inaccurate solution. When this happens, you can

1. Try a different initialization.

2. Use the Find other command. This is especially useful for finding other local minima to a minimization problem, or other local maxima to a maximization problem.

3. Adjust the accuracy setting (select Options/Settings). Often more accurate solutions can be obtained by merely changing the accuracy to be closer to zero.

4. Reformulate the problem.

More general considerations to keep in mind when formulating your problem include:

1. When setting up an equation file, it is important to remember to include all the constraints.

   Variables are not always positive. For instance, if you want to minimize $(x + 1/x)$, you probably want to require that $x > 0$.

2. Put in starting values when possible. Otherwise, Eureka may start its search at some random point that is very far from the solution and thus may not find the solution.

3. Use soft constraints where appropriate.

   A hard constraint is a condition that absolutely must be met for the solution to be useful; a soft constraint is more flexible. The following minimization has only a hard constraint:

   ```
   $ min(z)
   5 = x + w + y + z
   x <= 10
   w >= 0
   y >= 0
   ```

The constraint on x, to be equal to or less than 10, corresponds to a curve with infinite slope. If this were a cost curve, it would be untenable.

To alleviate this difficulty, you might recast the problem as:

```
$ min(z)
5 = x + w + y + z
x <= 10 + z
w >= 0
y >= 0
```

The slope now has a definable limit.

4. Assign names to constants.

Instead of this user-defined function containing numeric constants,

```
f(x) := 4.7 * exp(-2.1 * x + 1)
```

use this modification, inserting letters for the constants:

```
f(x) := A * exp(-B * x + 1)
A = 4.7
B = 2.1
```

This does not create extra work for Eureka, and it makes it easier for you to rerun the equation file with different parameters.

5. Try setting the *substlevel* setting to different values.

Eureka tries to be clever about making symbolic substitutions before it does a numerical search. Usually, this speeds up the numerical search, but sometimes the substitutions convert the problem to a form in which the search is more difficult. In these cases, sometimes it helps to lower *substlevel* — the number of substitutions Eureka is allowed to make during a search.

Substlevel can have any value from 0 to 6, with 6 as the default. If *substlevel* = 0, Eureka performs no substitutions. This can be useful (see Chapter 6, Problem 6 for an example where *substlevel* = 0 produces the solution to a complicated problem).

6. Avoid using badly scaled variables and functions.

For example,

```
x = 7
```

and

```
0.0000001 * x = 0.0000007
```

have the same solution mathematically, but computers sometimes cannot handle equations such as the second one very well because the difference in scale between the constant (0.0000001) and the variable ($x = 7$) is several orders of magnitude.

Eureka might conclude that $x = 1$ is a good approximation, since the difference between the right- and left-hand sides is only 0.0000006.

Refer to Chapter 6, Problem 15, for an example in which poorly scaled variables and functions cause Eureka great difficulty in solving a problem.

If Eureka encounters a syntax error in the equation file, it displays an appropriate error message. If this happens when you tell Eureka to Solve an equation file, refer to Appendix E for an explanation of the error message, then modify the equation file as necessary to correct the error.

Sometimes floating-point errors occur in the process of finding a solution. Floating-point errors do not necessarily invalidate a solution; they may mean only that Eureka used inappropriate numbers in the search. For example, in solving

$1/x = 10$

Eureka may try $x = 0$ before the correct solution of $x = 0.1$. Because division by zero results in floating-point overflow, the solution appears with a message:

```
Warning: floating point overflow
```

Similarly, Eureka may try to take a square root of a negative number while searching for a solution and issue a warning to that effect.

If a floating-point error does occur, it's a good idea to use the Verify or Iterate commands to validate the solution.

Menu Commands and Settings

This chapter describes Eureka's commands and settings that you select from the main menu or a submenu.

The descriptions are arranged first by main menu item (Commands, Graph, Report, and so on). Then, under each menu item heading, the descriptions are arranged in the order they appear on the menu.

Each description includes the name of the command or setting, followed by a discussion of the command's or setting's purpose, effect, and notable features.

The menu commands provide a way for you to direct the program and to make things happen. A command specifies a particular kind of operation that the computer is to perform. For instance, the File/Save command instructs Eureka to incorporate all newly entered text into the current file in memory and then save it (write it to disk).

Settings are those program parameters that you can change in the equation file, such as the number of digits displayed for values. Settings remain in effect throughout the entire work session. When you exit Eureka, the settings revert to their default values. You can save default settings with the Write setup command.

Main Menu

The main menu displays the fundamental program commands and setting groups:

File
: a group of commands that perform operations on files; also allows you to access DOS.

Edit
: allows you to create a new file, or change an existing one.

Solve
: finds the value of the variable(s) in the equation file.

Commands
: a group of commands that perform operations that supplement Solve.

Report
: a group of commands that produce a report based on the current equation file.

Graph
: a group of commands that generate plots or tables of values for the current equation file.

Options
: allows you to change default settings or selected variables.

Windows
: a group of commands that allow you to move and manipulate windows.

To select a command, type either the first letter of its name or cursor to the command you want and press *Enter*.

In most cases you select a setting in the same way. However, in some instances you select a setting by toggling a word (such as YES or NO) with the *Enter* key. The screen menu will prompt you for the correct response.

Table 4-1 summarizes the functions of the menu commands and settings, also in order of screen appearance.

Following Table 4-1, complete descriptions of each command and setting round out this section.

Table 4-1 *Main Menu And Submenu Summary*

Entry	Option	Description
FILE	Load	Bring an existing file to the screen
	New	Open a new file for editing
	Save	Write the current file to disk
	Write to..	Save the current file under the file name you specify
	Directory	List files in the specified directory
	Change dir	Change the active drive/directory
	Rename	Rename a file
	OS shell	Temporarily exit to DOS
	Quit	Leave Eureka and return to DOS
EDIT		Create a new file or modify an existing file
SOLVE		Find the value of the specified variable(s)
COMMANDS	Verify	Evaluate both sides of the equation and compare the result
	Calculator	Open a window in which arithmetic functions can be solved
	Find other	Search another area for the value of the specified variable
	Iterate	Continue iterating the value of the specified variable
REPORT	Go	Print/save a report about an equation file
	Output	Specify output device
	Formatted	Put report into formatted form
	Capture	Log your work to a file on disk
	Log file name	Specify name for capture file
GRAPH	Plot	Plot a graph of a user-defined function
	Output	Specify output device
	List	Generate a table of values for a user-defined function
	Function	Enter function to allow plotting or graphing
OPTIONS	Variables	Change value of variables(s) or constants
	Settings	Open a submenu of user-modifiable settings
	accuracy	Set stopping point for iterative searches
	casefold	Let upper and lowercase letters define different variables
	complex	Let variables be complex numbers
	digits	Set number of displayed digits
	finanmode	Set odd period as beginning or end
	finansmooth	Make financial functions smooth
	initval	Initialize variable
	list_first	Set first table value
	list_inc	Set increment for table
	list_num	Number of values in table
	listdefault	Override the default list settings

Table 4-1 *Main Menu And Submenu Summary, continued*

	maxtime	Set time limit for solving
	penalty	Determine relative weight of constraints
	plot_left	Set left endpoint of plot
	plot_right	Set right endpoint of plot
	plotdefault	Override the default plot endpoints
	radius	Set range of solve search
	rootsign	Set roots all negative or positive
	substlevel	Set level of internal substitution in solving
	syntax	Set syntax for arithmetic expressions
	Colors	Change window colors
	Directories	Specify where Eureka looks for its files
	Load setup	Let a predefined group of settings be used
	Write setup	Save a group of settings as a file
WINDOWS	Open	Open the specified window
	Close	Close the active window
	Next	Open and make active the next window
	Zoom	Expand the active window to fill the screen
	Tile	Make all open windows visible and of equal size
	Stack	Stack open windows at largest possible size
	Goto	Go to the active window

The File Commands

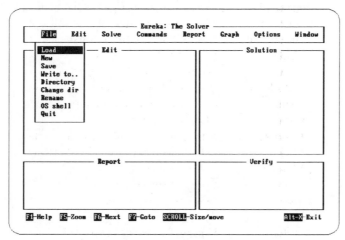

Figure 4-1   The File Menu

File

Press	*F*
Function	Enables you to select one of the File commands from the File menu.
Description	The File commands, in order of appearance in the File menu, are: Load, New, Save, Write to..., Directory, Change dir, Rename, OS shell, and Quit.
	The File commands are described in the order they appear on the menu.

Load

Press	*F L*
Function	Brings a copy of an existing file from disk to the screen, or names the edit buffer with a new file name.
Description	When you select Load, a prompt appears

```
Load File name
```

Type the name of the desired file, followed by *Enter*. You can specify a file on another drive or in another directory by specifying the full path name (for example, B:\PROBLEMS\FILENAME). You can also use wildcards (* or ?) to see a list of files; you can then choose the file you want to load. For example, you could type *.EKA to see all files with the .EKA extension.

Once you have entered the file name, Eureka reads the file from disk (or opens a new file if there is no existing file by that name) and displays it in the Edit window. Select Edit to activate the Eureka editor.

New

Press	*F N*
Function	Opens a new unnamed file for editing and activates the Eureka editor.
Description	When you select New, Eureka opens the Edit window. You can then create a new equation file. When you want to save the file, select Save or Write to...

Save

Press	*F S*
Function	Incorporates your latest changes to the named file in the Edit window and writes a copy of the changed file to disk.
Description	When you select Save, Eureka writes a copy of the file in the Edit window to the current directory or to another directory/drive if you specify a path name. The file remains on the screen so you can continue editing or solve the equations.

Save does not save plots or tables that you generate with the Graph command. To save a copy of a plot or table, use the Report command.

Save creates a backup file with the extension .BAK each time you save a file. If for some reason your original file is corrupted, you can always load the .BAK file.

Write to...

Press	*F W*
Function	Allows you to give a name to the file you are editing and save it to disk.
Description	Write to... offers an easy way to make files that are variations of each other. When you select Write to... a prompt appears

`New name`

To save a file incorporating your current changes, type a name and then press *Enter*. You can make changes to your file as many times as you like, each time saving the variations to disk under a different file name.

Directory

Press	*F D*
Function	Displays all or some of the files and subdirectories on the current directory or disk.
Description	When you select Directory, a prompt appears

`Enter mask`

The term *mask*, as used in Eureka, refers to a group of characters that you type in order to search selectively for a file (or group of files) or some other object.

To view the contents of the current directory, press *Enter*. A window appears, listing all the files in the directory. To view only certain files in the directory, type an appropriate mask followed by *Enter*. Eureka displays a selected listing to be displayed. Pressing *Esc* returns you to the main menu.

With a mask, you can screen the contents of a directory by using the two DOS wildcards: the asterisk (*) and the question mark (?).

The * wildcard tells the computer to find all matching character strings, starting from the position of the *. For example, you could use * to display all files starting with the letters AN by typing AN*.* as the mask. Or, to search for a file that starts with Math and ends with the extension CAL, you would type Math*.CAL as the mask.

The ? wildcard works similarly to the * wildcard, except ? finds only one character at a time. For example, to search for the following files

AMT12OPA
AMT43OPB
AMT89OPA

you would enter the mask AMT??OP?; Eureka will list these files (and any others with the same characters in the first, second, third, sixth, and seventh positions).

You can also view a list of files in any other directory by specifying the path name of the directory.

To view all the files in a subdirectory, move the cursor to the subdirectory name in the file list and press *Enter*.

Change dir

Press   F C

Function   Changes the current drive/directory.

Description   When you select Change dir, a prompt appears

    `Enter dir name`

To change the current drive/directory, type the full path name of the desired directory (and the drive name if you are changing drives), followed by *Enter*. The usual drives are A, B, or C, unless you have a RAM disk or are using a network (in that case, the directory can be D: or higher).

Eureka will now look for files on the new directory. If the requested directory does not exist, Eureka will display an error message.

Rename

Press   F R

Function   Renames the file in the Edit window.

Description   When you select Rename, a prompt appears:

    `Enter name`

Enter a new name for the file in the Edit window, then press *Enter*. Eureka renames the file in memory *only*. Use Save to save the file with the new name to disk.

OS shell

Press	*F O*
Function	Allows you to access DOS without removing Eureka from memory.
Description	When you select OS shell, Eureka disappears from the screen (but not from memory), and the DOS prompt (>) comes up.

To execute any DOS command, type the command followed by *Enter*.

To return to Eureka, type EXIT.

Quit

Press	*F Q*
Function	Leaves Eureka and returns to DOS.
Description	When you select Quit, you will be returned to DOS. If you have not saved the file in the Edit window, Eureka will ask you if you want to save it. If you don't save, any changes you've made to it will be lost.

The Edit Command

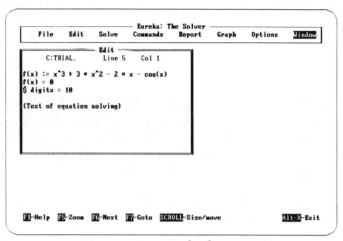

Figure 4-2 *Typical Edit Screen*

Edit

Press	*E*
Function	Activates the Eureka editor. Using the editor, you can either modify an existing file or create a new one.
Description	When you select Edit, the Edit window becomes active. You can create a new equation file or edit an existing one.

    To create a new file, just type in your file. When you want to save it, select Write To... from the File menu.

    To edit an existing file, select Load from the File menu, then type the file's name (using its full path name if necessary) followed by *Enter*.

    The editor uses a combination of standard control character sequences and predefined function keys for editing. It is virtually identical to Borland's Turbo Pascal and SideKick editors. To switch between Insert and Overwrite modes, press *Ins*.

    More detailed information about the editor can be found in Chapter 2 and Appendix B.

The Solve Command

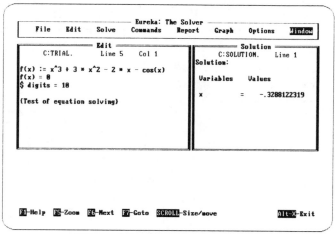

Figure 4-3 *Typical Solve Screen*

Solve

Press	S
Function	Finds a value for each variable in an equation file that satisfies the constraints of the equation file.
Description	For each variable, Solve finds the first value that satisfies the constraints of an equation. If a problem cannot be solved directly (by plugging in a formula), it is recast as a minimization. Eureka then checks for a user-supplied initialization value (using the value 1 if none is supplied) and begins to iterate toward a minimum. Once Eureka finds a solution, the Solution window displays all variables and their solved values.

You can interrupt a search for a solution by pressing *Ctrl-Break*. Eureka then gives the current values of the variables. To continue the search, press *Esc* and select Iterate from the Commands menu.

Many problems have multiple solutions. Eureka's search method finds only one at a time. You can find other solutions by using different starting values, by adding constraints that exclude undesirable solutions, or by using the Find other command on the Commands menu.

Eureka can find the roots of polynomials. Consider an equation file containing a function defined as a polynomial in one variable:

$p(x) := \text{poly}(x,1,0,0,0,1)$

Applying Solve to the file causes Eureka to find all of the roots of $p(x)$ as well as to solve for whatever other variables appear in the file.

The Commands Commands

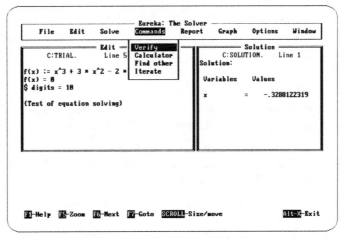

Figure 4-4   *The Commands Menu*

Commands

Press	C
Function	The Commands menu contains commands that perform mathematical operations on elements in the equation file.
Description	The commands, in order of appearance in the Commands menu, are: Verify, Calculator, Find other, and Iterate.

Verify

Press	C V
Function	Evaluates all expressions in an equation file and compares the results on an equation-by-equation basis.
Description	You use the Verify command primarily to verify the accuracy of a previously computed result. A typical command cycle for solving problems is:

- Edit (to create a problem)
- Solve (to find a solution)

- Verify (to verify the accuracy)
- Report (to print the results)

When you select Verify, Eureka goes through all equations and inequalities in the equation file and evaluates every expression, substituting in the previously solved values for variables. During an evaluation, Eureka ignores all directives and initializations, solves none of the equations, and changes none of the variable values.

When the evaluation is complete, Eureka displays the results with any discrepancies in the Verify window.

If the difference indicates that an equation or inequality is invalid (the difference is greater than that allowed by the accuracy setting), the difference is flagged as an error.

For example, if a file contains the following obviously incorrect equation

```
1/3 = 10 * exp(1)
```

the Verify window shows this result:

```
1/3 = 0.33333
10 * exp(1) = 27.18282
difference (error) = -26.84948
```

Calculator

Press	C C
Function	Lets you perform arithmetic calculations in display-calculator fashion.
Description	The Calculator command acts as a shortcut: use it to evaluate an arithmetic expression when you don't want to make a new equation file.

Eureka's Calculator can handle any built-in function as long as it does not require an undefined variable.

When you select Calculator from the Commands menu, an empty Calculator window appears on the screen. Type in an expression such as

```
10 * exp(1) - 7
```

followed by *Enter*, and Eureka displays the value of the expression.

An arithmetic expression is limited to one line of 29 characters, unless you expand the window with the arrow keys after pressing *Scroll-Lock* and *Num-Lock*.

If there is a syntax error in the arithmetic expression, an error message appears.

If you have solved an equation file, you can insert variable names from the file into expressions in the Calculator, such as the variable *Depth* shown in the example below:

```
sin(Depth^2)
```

The pound symbol (#) has a special meaning in the Calculator: it contains the value of the previously evaluated expression.

Find other

Press	C F
Function	Tells Eureka to find another solution to the equation file, different from the one that Solve just generated.
Description	While Eureka is normally satisfied when it finds one solution to an equation file, many systems of equations have several distinct solutions. The solution you need may not be the first one that Eureka finds. When you select Find other, Eureka tries to find a solution that is different from the solution(s) already obtained.
	You can use Find other repeatedly to find multiple solutions. For example, Find other can find additional local minima to a minimization problem. (**Note:** In such a minimization problem, you can also use the Variable setting to help Eureka start a new search in a different range of numbers.)

Iterate

Press	C I
Function	Continues solving a problem that has been Solved at least once.
Description	Sometimes, Eureka is unable to solve a set of equations directly. If this occurs, the program uses an iterative method to obtain better and better approximations until the solutions satisfy certain convergence criteria. However, you may think that the program has given up too soon, settling for a solution that meets the accuracy require-

ments, but stops short of the best solution. If you think this has happened, select the Iterate command and Eureka will continue solving where it left off.

You can also use the Iterate command to resume a search that has been interrupted with *Ctrl-Break*.

The Report Commands

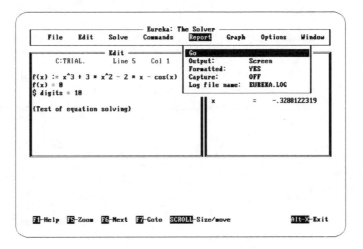

Figure 4-5   *The Report Menu*

Report

Press	*R*
Function	Enables you to select one of the Report commands from the Report menu. The Report commands prepare a report of the solved equation file and then send it to a specified output device. Reports are formatted for a standard 66-line, 80-column printer.

A report consists of:

- a header with date, time, and file name information
- the equation file
- the solution (as displayed in the Solution window)
- the evaluation (as displayed in the Verify window)
- the most recently generated graph or table

Description	The Report commands, in order of appearance in the Reports menu, are: Go, Output, Formatted, Capture, and Log file name.

Go

Press   *R G*

Function   Sends a report in the specified format to the previously specified output device.

Description   You use Go after you have set the format and output device for the report (use the Formatted and Output commands to set these report features). See Chapter 6 for examples of finished reports.

Output

Press   *R O* < s, f, or p >

Function   Determines where Eureka sends a report: to the screen (s), to a file (f), or to a printer (p).

Description   Select one of three possible values for output by highlighting the option you want, then pressing **Enter**. The report destinations are:

- Screen — (the default) sends the report to the screen
- File — sends the report to a disk file
- Printer — sends the report to a printer

When you select File, then select Go, a prompt appears:

    Output file name

Type a file name just as you would for an equation file. The report is saved to disk.

Once saved as a file, you can edit a report like an equation file with the Eureka editor or any ASCII text editor. However, no mathematical operations (such as Solve) can be performed on a report file.

Formatted

Press	*R F* < y or n >
Function	Determines whether or not a report is formatted. Default is *yes*.
Description	A formatted report is designed to go to a printer from your computer and has the following features:

- 1/2-inch left margin (rather than printing flush with the edge of the paper)
- incorporates page breaks

If you intend to edit the report with a different text editor before printing it, you should select Formatted/*no*.

To toggle between Formatted/*yes* (the default) and Formatted/ *no*, press **Enter**.

When Eureka sends a formatted report to a printer, printing starts at the top of the page. If you want blank lines at the top of the page, position the printer appropriately.

Capture

Press	*R C*
Function	Automatically writes work session into a file periodically.
Description	Capture is useful for automatically saving your work to guard against power failures. It is also useful when you want to solve a series of problems and save all your work to a file. When you select Capture, you toggle Capture *on* and *off*. With Capture *on*, your work will be continuously saved to the file name specified by Log file name.

Log file name

Press	*R L*
Function	Specifies a file name to be used by the Capture command; the default name is EUREKA.LOG.

The Graph Commands

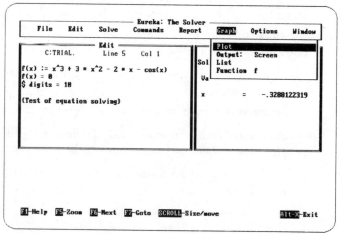

Figure 4-6 *The Graph Menu*

Graph

Press	G
Function	Enables you to select one of the commands from the Graph menu. The Graph commands generate and display on-screen plots of functions and tables of values.
Description	The Graph commands, in order of appearance in the Graph menu, are: Plot, Output, List, and Function.

Plot

Press	G P
Function	Plots a function on the screen.
Description	Eureka can plot functions on the screen, even on a computer without a graphics card. Eureka can only plot user-defined functions of exactly one variable. For example, the function $\sin(x) + 0.1 \times x$ can be plotted if the following definition of the function appears in the equation file:

```
f(x) := sin(x) + 0.1 * x
```

When you select the Graph menu, the Plot command is available only if at least one user-defined function of a single variable appears in the just-solved equation file. If the Plot command is not available, it is displayed in half intensity on the Graph menu.

If no appropriate function exists in the equation file or if there is no just-solved equation file, you can use the Function command to write a function directly to Eureka.

If more than one user-defined, single-variable function appears in the equation file, a list of choices appears, prompting you to select the name of the function you intend to plot.

When you have selected the function to be plotted, a prompt appears immediately, requesting the left and right endpoints (lower and upper limits of the variable).

Enter the left value, then press *Enter* and repeat for the right value. If you hit *Enter* without selecting lower and upper limits to the variable, Eureka either resorts to its default values, -2 and 10, or whatever values you have specified in the Settings menu for plot_left and plot_right. Eureka scales the vertical axis automatically.

Using your selection of left and right endpoints for the horizontal axis, Eureka displays the plot in a window on the screen; you can save the plot in a report with the Report commands.

You can change the default values for several settings that govern the plot (see plot_left, plot_right, and plotdefault under the Options/Settings menu). If you have a graphics card in your computer, you can see a graphic display of your plot by pressing the Zoom key (*F5*).

Output

Press	*G O* < s or p >
Function	Determines where Eureka sends a plot: to the screen (s) or the printer (p).
Description	By default, Eureka will send your plot to the screen. If you press *P*, Eureka sends the plot to a printer (must be Epson-compatible).

Press	*G L*
Function	Computes a table of values for a function, then displays the table on screen.
Description	The List command creates a two-column table (a set of ordered pairs of numbers) for a function. The table represents the same information that would appear in a graph of the function but with greater precision.

The List command, like Plot, acts on user-defined functions of one variable. Eureka prompts you for:

1. the first value of the function argument

2. the increment

3. the number of points (200 is the maximum allowed)

For example, given the function $f(x) := x^2$, with:

First point: 3
Increment: 1
Number of values: 5

Eureka returns the following table:

x	$f(x)$
3	9.000
4	16.000
5	25.000
6	36.000
7	49.000

You can use the Report menu to save your tables in report files or print them as hard copy.

You can change the default values for several settings that govern the list (see list_first, list_inc, and list_num on page 73).

Press	*G F*
Function	Allows you to enter a function of one variable that can then be plotted or listed.
Description	If an equation file does not contain a user-defined function, this command provides an alternate way to list or plot an equation. You can use this feature by itself or in conjunction with an equation file.

When you select Function, a prompt appears:

`Enter function`

Type the appropriate function name; for example, $f(x)$, followed by *Enter*. Another prompt appears:

`Enter function definition`

Type the definition (for example, x^3), followed by *Enter*.

The function name and the definition are each limited to 18 characters.

When you have entered the function name and definition, use the cursor keys to move to the Plot or List options.

If your equation file contains a user-defined function, you can bypass the Function command and go directly to Plot or List.

The Options Commands

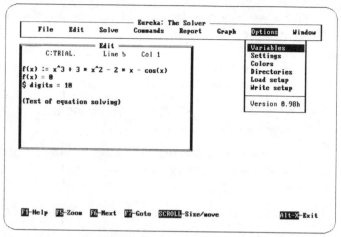

Figure 4-7   The Options Menu

Options

Press	O
Function	Enables you to select one of the commands from the Options menu.

The Options commands allow you to temporarily change some of Eureka's internal information and screen appearance, as well as write or read a setup file. Settings remain in effect throughout the work session. When you exit Eureka, the settings revert to their default values (unless you select Write setup).

Description	The Options commands, in order of appearance in the Options menu, are: Variables, Settings, Colors, Directories, Load setup, and Write setup.

Variables

Press	O V
Function	Lets you restart Eureka's solving procedure using a new initial value; it also lets you change the value of a constant.

Description   After Eureka solves an equation file, select Variables to display a window of any active variables and constants.

To modify any of the displayed items:

1. Use the cursor keys to select the desired item. Press *Enter.*

2. Type in a new value.

3. Press *Enter.*

To reactivate the main menu and re-solve the problem, press *Esc Esc*, then press *S*. If the problem has already been solved, press *Esc Esc C I* to reactivate the main menu.

The Variables command is useful when the first solution Eureka finds is not the one you want. (Problems often have more than one solution, though only one may be appropriate.)

For example, in the case of a polynomial, Eureka starts from some initial solution and iterates toward a final solution. While most equations are readily solved this way, others are not. This is because an initialization value might be selected that leads Eureka off into a local minima that is not the true solution. Whenever you suspect this is the case, use Variables to re-examine the problem.

This is an example of a situation where you could use the Variables command:

Suppose that Eureka is to minimize $(\exp(x) - a \times 2)$ for various values of a. You could type this into the equation file:

```
y = (exp(x) - a * 2)
a = 3
$ min(y)
```

After the solution appears, choosing Variables reveals that x and y are active variables and that a is a constant.

Note: If a had been initialized to 3 $(a := 3)$ rather than set equal to 3, it would appear as an additional active variable and not as a constant.

If you change a to some other value and select Iterate, Eureka can find a minimum value for y using the new value of a.

Using the Variables command, a whole sequence of problems can be solved without changing the equation file.

Press	O S
Function	Lets you alter selected settings for the current equation file.

When you select Settings, a submenu appears, listing each modifiable setting, the setting's current default value, and the value's type (real number, integer, and so on). One of the settings is highlighted.

To make a selection from this menu:

1. Use the arrow keys to highlight the setting you plan to change.

2. Type the new value for the setting (or press *Enter* for *yes/no* toggles).

3. Press *Esc*.

Enter the new value in the same format as the default value, which is the middle item in the highlighted line.

For example, to set *complex*, press *Enter* to toggle it to *yes*.

Description   A number of settings can be changed from the Options/Settings menu item. You can also change most of these settings by inserting a directive in the equation file. There are six settings that *cannot* be changed via this menu: *include, maximize, minimize, settings, solve,* and *unit conversions.* See Chapter 5, "Directives," for information about these directives.

The settings that *can* be controlled from the Settings menu are:

accuracy	listdefault
casefold	maxtime
complex	penalty
digits	plot_left
finanmode	plot_right
finansmooth	plotdefault
initval	radius
list_first	rootsign
list_inc	substlevel
list_num	syntax

All of these settings except list_first, list_inc, list_num, plot_left, and plot_right can be used as directives (see "Directives" in Chapter 5 for more information about these settings).

The seven non-directive settings are described as follows:

listdefault   Options: < yes or no >
         Default: no

Determines whether values specified for list_first, list_inc, and list_num are used. When set to *yes*, these values are used; when *no*, you are prompted to enter values.

list_first   Options: < any negative or positive number >
         Default: 0.000000

Sets a new default value for the first variable to be solved for in a table of values for the listed function.

list_inc   Options: < any negative or positive number >
         Default: 0.500000

Sets a new default value for the increment between values to be solved for in a table of values for the function.

list_num   Options: < the integers 1 through 200 >
         Default: 10

Sets a new default value for the number of values to be solved for in a table of values for the function.

plotdefault   Options: < yes or no >
         Default: no

Determines whether values specified for plot_left and plot_right are used. When set to *yes*, these values are used; when *no*, you are prompted to enter values.

plot_left   Options: < any negative or positive number >
         Default: −2

Sets a new default value for the left-most point at which the plot of the function begins.

plot_right   Options: < any negative or positive number >
         Default: 10

Sets a new default value for the right-hand side of the plot of the function. The value must be greater than the value set for plot_left.

Colors

Press   O C

Function   Lets you change the window colors.

Description When you select Colors, Eureka calls up a windows menu to the center of the screen. Move the highlighted bar up and down in the window with the arrow keys. When the block highlights the name of the window to be changed, press *Enter*. A blank sample version of the selected window appears on the screen.

To change the window's colors, use the up and down arrow keys to select background, text, or margin (items in the status line), then use the left and right arrow keys to toggle the color of the selected item in the sample window. When the item displays in the color you want, press *Enter*.

To save these changes in a setup file, select Write setup.

Directories

Press   O D

Function   Determines where Eureka stores its files.

Description When you select Directories, Eureka presents you with a list of two kinds of files: Eureka dir and Problem files. Use the arrow keys to highlight a selection and press *Enter*. Eureka then prompts you for the path name of the directory where you want to store your files. For instance, suppose you want to store your equation files in a subdirectory called C:\EUREKA\PROBLEMS and the Eureka program itself in a directory C:\EUREKA. Enter the full path name for each type of file. From now on, your equation files will be automatically saved in the C:\EUREKA\PROBLEMS directory when you select Write to.. or Save on the Files menu, and Eureka will look for its program, help, and setup files in the Eureka directory.

Load setup

Press	*O L*
Function	Brings a file (created with the Write setup command) containing various setup parameters to the screen. These setup parameters will be used until you exit Eureka.
Description	When you select Load setup, a prompt appears

      `Enter file name`

      Type the full path name of the desired file, followed by *Enter*. If you specify no extension, the extension .EKA is automatically appended.

Write setup

Press	*O W*
Function	Saves a file containing various screen and printer parameters.
Description	When you select Write setup, Eureka saves the current setup file to disk. By default, Eureka looks for a file named INITIAL.EKA when it is first loaded. If you want to use a standard set of setup parameters when you load Eureka, name your file INITIAL.EKA. If you specify no extension, the file name extension .EKA is automatically appended.

      The modifiable Setup parameters include those for window size, placement, and screen colors.

The Window Commands

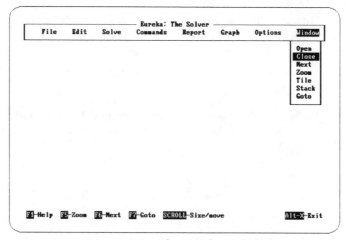

Figure 4-8   *The Window Menu*

Window

Press	W
Function	Selects one of the commands from the Window menu. These commands allow you to move and manipulate on-screen windows.
Description	The Window commands, in order of appearance on the Window menu, are: Open, Close, Next, Zoom, Tile, Stack, and Goto.

Open

Press	W O
Function	Opens the specified window.
Description	Opens one of Eureka's windows. When you select Open, Eureka presents you with a menu of all of Eureka's windows. Move the cursor down to the window you want to open, then press *Enter*.
	If several windows are currently displayed on the screen, you can move between them by pressing *F6*.

Close

Press   *W C*

Function   Closes the currently active window.

Description When you select Close, Eureka closes the currently active window and removes it from the screen. If you have several windows open, you can select Close repeatedly until all on-screen windows are closed.

Next

Press   *W N*

Function   Opens and makes active the next on-screen window.

Description Use Next to move back and forth between on-screen windows. If you select Next repeatedly, Eureka will activate each window in turn, moving in a clockwise direction.

The function key *F6* does exactly the same thing as the Next command.

Zoom

Press   *W Z*

Function   Expands the active window to fill the screen.

Description Use Zoom when you want the window you are currently working with to fill the screen. This might come in handy when you are working with an equation file that is too long to see with the default size Edit window. To "dezoom" the window, select Zoom again. The *F5* key does exactly the same thing as the Zoom command.

Tile

Press   *W T*

Function   Makes all open windows visible and of equal size.

Description The Tile command rearranges all on-screen windows so that that are aligned side by side in a tile-like pattern, each the same size.

Stack

Press   *W S*

Function   Stacks all on-screen windows on top of each other.

Description   The Stack command stacks all on-screen windows atop each other in the center of the screen. Windows are expanded to fill the entire screen.

You can move back and forth between windows by pressing *F6* or by selecting the Next command. This "reshuffles" the windows so that the selected window is on top.

Goto

Press   *W G*

Function   Puts the cursor in the last active window.

Description   The *F7* key does the same thing as Goto.

The Equation File:
Syntax, Directives, and Functions

This chapter describes the equation file:

- what goes into an equation file
- what the syntax of an equation file must be
- what the equation file directives are and what they do
- what built-in and user-defined functions are; how they are alike, how they differ
- what causes Eureka to return an error message

Chapter 2 explains the Eureka editor and how to create the equation file; it includes a discussion of predefined keys and illustrations of the Edit window, the Solution window, and the Verify window. Chapter 3 provides tips for writing good equation files. Appendix C describes all the built-in functions.

Contents of the Equation File

An equation file must contain one or more equations, as well as initialization values and user-defined functions when needed. It may also contain directives and comments.

Equations are mathematical statements that consist of two expressions (sometimes more) connected by an equal sign (=) or a relational operator (< or >). The following are examples of equations that can be used in a Eureka equation file:

```
y = x^3 + 2 * x + x - 4
sin((x + 2 * pi)/3) > cos((x - pi)/4)
y^2 - x < x^2 + 2 * x * y
```

An *expression* is composed of one or more terms connected by an algebraic operator.

A *term* is either a numeric value, a variable name, or a function.

The argument of a function may in turn be a variable, a constant, or a term.

Algebraic operators are:

*	multiply
/	divide
+	add
−	subtract
^	raise to the power

Typically, you write one equation per line. However, you can use a colon (:) to separate equations appearing on the same line. The colon is useful when you want to define the constraints that limit a variable. For example, you could enter the constraint

```
0 < x
```

and

```
x = 2 * y
```

in an equation file as the following two equations:

```
0 < x : x = 2 * y
```

Eureka uses standard algebraic notation to describe equations (also called formulas) and applies standard algebraic operator precedence (exponents first, right-to-left; multiplication and division next, left-to-right; addition and subtraction last, left-to-right).

There can be up to twenty equations in any one equation file.

Initialization Values

Initialization sets specific values, either for a variable or for the starting point of an iterative search.

An initialization differs from an equation in that Eureka is not required to keep a variable at the initial value. An initialization value should be slightly higher than the value being sought.

Initializations are flagged with the symbol := and are written one per line. The symbol := means "is initially set at the value ."

For example, $x := 3$ means x is initially set at the value 3. Eureka will plug the value 3 for x into the equation file and evaluate all related expressions, then continue to modify the value of x (from the initial value of 3) and plug in the modified value until some value of x solves the equations.

Initialization values only affect formulas that Eureka solves iteratively and not directly (by algorithm).

If you do not set an initial value for a variable, Eureka uses the default value, 1.

User-defined Functions

User-defined functions satisfy two needs: They provide a way to define complicated functions, and they allow Eureka to generate plots and tables.

Like initialization values, user-defined functions are also flagged by the symbol := and are written one per line. In the case of user-defined functions, the symbol := reads "is defined as ." User-defined functions differ from initialization values in that the left-hand expression is a function of some variable(s), and is not just a variable or term.

For example, the following are bona fide, user-defined functions:

```
f(x,y) := (x^2)/4 + (y^2)/3
g(z) := z^3 + 2 * z^2 + 5 * z - 13
```

The first of these two user-defined functions reads:

the function f of x and y is defined as $\dfrac{x^2}{4} + \dfrac{y^2}{3}$.

Eureka's built-in polynomial and differential functions (*poly* and *deriv*) must be written as user-defined functions.

You can use up to ten (but no more) user-defined functions in an equation file.

Directives

Directives are commands to Eureka to do something out of the ordinary. Definitions of each Eureka directive are given later in this chapter.

Directives begin with a dollar sign ($) character, and are written one per line in the equation file; for example,

```
$ digits = 5
$ include "molewts"
$ rootsign = yes
```

The *settings* directive allows you to enter a cluster of directives without beginning each one with a $; this directive is explained fully under "Settings" in this chapter (see page 95).

There is no limit to the number of directives that you can use in any one equation file.

Comments

Comments typically describe the purpose of a particular file or individual lines. Use either a semicolon (;) or braces ({ }) to delimit comments. Some examples of comments include:

```
; This is a comment

x^2 + 2 * t^2 = 5 ; this part, after the semicolon, is a comment

{ This is also a comment }
{ Mortgage payments for new building site }
```

Notes On Equation File Syntax

Variable Names

Variable names are limited to 60 characters; all characters are significant. The first character in a variable name must be a letter. The remaining characters in the variable name (up to a total of 60) may be any alphanumeric.

By default, variables are case sensitive; you can alter this sensitivity with a *$ casefold* directive or setting. (*Case sensitive* means that Eureka sees variations like TEST, test, Test, and TEst as four different, unique variable names.)

Values and Precision

A *value* can be entered as a real number, a variable name, or an expression.

A real number entry can be 0, or it can have an absolute value between $1e - 308$ and $1e + 308$.

You can specify numeric values in either standard decimal notation or scientific notation. Internally, Eureka maintains 16 decimal places.

Eureka ignores leading zeroes. Also, commas have no numeric significance; they are used to separate arguments in functions.

Mathematical Operators and Order of Evaluation

The following symbols specify the standard arithmetic operators:

+   addition

−   subtraction

*   multiplication

/   division

^   exponentiation

~   complex conjugate of function

Arithmetic expressions are evaluated in the following order and direction:

Operator	Order of Evaluation	Direction
~, exp, sin, etc.	1 (first)	left-to-right
^	2 .	right-to-left
*, /	3 .	left-to-right
+, −	4 .	left-to-right
=, <, >, < >, < =, > =	5 (last)	left-to-right

For example, Eureka evaluates the following expression:

```
~U * V - x * y/z + A^B^C
```

as

$$[(\sim U) \ * \ V] \ - \frac{x \ * \ y}{z} \ + \ (A)\char`^(B\char`^C)$$

See the description of the *syntax* directive in this chapter for more information about parentheses in order of evaluation.

Syntax Rules

Eureka is fairly lenient about what it considers to be a syntactically correct equation file. You need not enter the different parts of the equation file in any specific order as long as each equation, comment, directive, initialization, and user-defined function is properly set up.

Eureka follows these syntax rules:

1. All spaces and tabs are ignored. Blank lines are permitted.

2. Multiple formula relations are allowed, as with

    ```
    t = r^2 = x^2 + y^2
    ```

    or

    ```
    0 < x < 1
    ```

3. A colon (:) can be used to separate formulas on the same line. For example, the above multiple relations are equivalent to

    ```
    T = r^2 : r^2 = x^2 + y^2
    ```

    and

    ```
    0 < x : x < 1
    ```

4. In units conversion, the colon is used in conjunction with an arrow (−>), formed by typing a dash followed by a greater-than symbol. Units conversion requires two directives: *units* and *end*

    ```
    $units
    cm -> in : x / 2.54
    $end
    ```

5. Comments may either be inserted to the right of a semicolon (;) on any line or enclosed in braces ({ }), as in

```
r^2 = x^2 + y^2 ; This is a comment
```

or

```
{ This file solves the ideal gas law, }
{ using mks units }
```

Mixing the two notations for comments can have unpredictable results and is not recommended.

6. An underscore character (_) means that the formula continues to the next line, as in

```
z = (x - a)^2 _
+ (y - b)^2
```

The underscore character is unnecessary if the upper line is an incomplete formula, as in

```
z = (x - a)^2 +
(y - b)^2
```

7. A tilde (~) gives the complex conjugate of a function, as in

```
z = re(z) + im(z) * sqrt(-1)
~z = re(z) - im(z) * sqrt(-1)
abs(z) = sqrt(z * ~z)
```

8. Variables may be initialized with any valid arithmetic expression, such as

```
x := exp(1) * 3.14159/2
```

9. A directive is a line that has a dollar sign ($) as its first nonspace character.

Special Symbols

Most equation files consist of ordinary ASCII characters, but there are a few special IBM graphics characters that Eureka recognizes. These special symbols and their decimal values are:

- square root sign (251)
- greek letters (224 through 238, except 236)
- divide sign (246)
- greater-than-or-equal, less-than-or-equal (242, 243)
- two (253)
- one half, one quarter (171, 172)
- pi (227) (You can also get the pi symbol by pressing *Alt-P*.)

To use a special symbol in an equation file, hold down *Alt* and *Shift* while typing the symbol's value on the numeric keypad to the right of the keyboard (the one set up like a 10-key adding machine). For SuperKey users, the file EUREKA.MAC on the distribution disk contains macros for these special symbols.

Directives

A *directive* is a command to the Eureka program; it is embedded within an equation file and affects only that file. Most directives in Eureka affect the settings that are user controlled. There are a few others that perform different kinds of functions.

You can also change some settings from the Options menu. The settings stay in effect until you exit Eureka. You can also use the Load setup and Write setup commands to save and load settings. You can only make permanent setting changes within a given equation file by using directives.

The only directives (settings) that *cannot* be changed from the Options menu are: *include, maximize, minimize, settings, solve,* and *unit conversions.*

A directive consists of the symbol $ followed by the directive name, an equal sign (usually), and some value. For example, you can set the setting syntax to 2 in an equation file with the directive

```
$ syntax = 2
```

You can use the *settings* directive to enter a subgroup of the directives (those which affect Eureka's internal default settings) in an alternate format, illustrated here:

```
$ settings
syntax = 2
digits = 10
accuracy = 1e-13
penalty = 50
$ end
```

This format is convenient for changing multiple settings, since only two $ symbols are required. You can include as many directives as you need between *settings* and *end*.

If you have a group of non-default settings common to a number of problems, you can store them in a separate file. You can then insert this separate settings file into an equation file with the *include* directive.

For instance, the following directive would include a settings file called DEFAULTS:

```
$ include "DEFAULTS"
```

The directives are individually described in alphabetical order on the following pages. Each description includes the directive name, syntax (exactly how to type it), default value, function, and any pertinent remarks.

Syntax	`$ accuracy = <value>`
Default	.0000001 $(1.0e - 7)$
Function	Specifies a value that must be met before an iterative search stops.
Description	When Eureka reports a solution, it is not necessarily exact. In most cases, Eureka's iterative procedure searches for a solution until the accuracy matches the accuracy setting value.

The default value (.0000001) results in an answer that is accurate to six or seven decimal places. Eureka can achieve greater accuracy if you set the *accuracy* directive to a smaller value, such as

```
$ accuracy = 1.0e - 12
```

However, there are tradeoffs to using very small values for the accuracy. Smaller values increase computer processing time and could undermine the overall reliability of the solution procedure.

casefold

Syntax	`$ casefold = <yes or no>`
Default	No
Function	Changes Eureka's sensitivity to the case of variable names.
Description	The default allows uppercase and lowercase letters to be used as different, unique characters; by default, Eureka considers *pressure* and *Pressure* to be two different variables.

If you change *casefold* to *yes*, Eureka will consider the uppercase and lowercase versions of any letter as only one variable.

Key words (directives, and so on) and built-in functions are never affected by *casefold* and are not case sensitive. For example, the exponential function can be written exp(x), Exp(x), or EXP(x).

complex (numbers)

Syntax	`$ complex = <yes or no>`
Default	No
Function	Makes all variables complex.

Description   When *complex = no*, Eureka cannot solve equations whose solutions have a non-zero imaginary component, except for polynomials solved with the *poly* function.

For example, it is impossible to solve the following equation without using complex numbers, since its solutions are $x = (3 + i)$ and $x = (3 - i)$:

```
x^2 - 6 * x + 10 = 0
```

However, Eureka can find a complex solution if you change the mode to complex, either from the Settings menu or by putting the *complex* directive in the equation file.

While Eureka is operating in complex mode, the functions *exp*, *ln*, *sin*, *cos*, *tan*, and *sqrt* refer to their analytic continuations. (A branch cut is used for *ln*, *sqrt*, and exponentiation.)

Re and *im* are the real and imaginary parts, respectively. The tilde ($\sim$) gives the complex conjugate. By this definition,

```
z = re(z) + im(z) * sqrt(-1)
~z = re(z) - im(z) * sqrt(-1)
abs(z) = sqrt(z * ~z)
```

When maximizing or minimizing a complex function, Eureka uses only the real part.

Similarly, $<$, $>$, and *polar* refer only to the real parts of the expressions they operate on. Usually, however, these expressions are arranged so as to be real, as in

```
abs(z) < 100
```

The best way to obtain complex constants is to assign an imaginary value to some variable (typically *i* or *I*). The following example illustrates this technique:

$$i = \text{sqrt}(-1)$$
$$z = 2 + 3 * i$$

digits

Syntax $ digits = <integer from 1 to 13>

Default   8

Function   Sets the number of digits displayed for solved variables.

Description   The *digits* directive tells Eureka to display only the specified number of digits for values in the Solution window.

This directive only affects the way in which Eureka displays real numbers and is unrelated to the underlying accuracy of the solutions.

end

Syntax   `$ end`

Default   None

Function   Completes a list of directives begun with either a *settings* or *units* directive.

Description   See the descriptions for *settings* and *units*.

finanmode

Syntax   `$ finanmode = <begin or end>`

Default   End

Function   Sets the odd financial period (if there is one) to be at either the end or the beginning of the series of periods used for calculations made with the financial functions.

Description   Changing *finanmode* to *begin* puts the odd period at the beginning and results in slightly different values for the functions *pval*, *paymt*, and *fval*.

finansmooth

Syntax   `$ finansmooth = <yes or no>`

Default   No

Function   Determines whether the *pval, paymt,* and *fval* functions are smooth.

Description   The financial functions, *pval, paymt,* and *fval,* are discontinuous as functions of time. This is because the value of a loan contract changes at the end (or beginning) of each period, every time a payment is made. These discontinuities make solving for the time variable difficult or impossible.

You can use the *finansmooth* directive to circumvent this problem. When you set *finansmooth* to *yes*, *pval*, *paymt*, and *fval* become smooth functions. These smoothed functions are exactly correct if the time is an integer; if time is not an integer, they return interpolated values which may differ somewhat from the true values.

include

Syntax	`$ include "<filename>"`
Default	None
Function	Inserts a second file into the body of a first.
Description	The way files are included in Eureka is similar to the way they are commonly included in programming languages. This directive is provided as an editing convenience. When Eureka processes an equation file with an *include* directive, it replaces the directive with the named file. This keeps your equation files from becoming unnecessarily large and unwieldy.

Include files are primarily useful for storing unit conversions and set-up options separately, so they can easily be used in a number of problems. They are also useful for storing frequently used data, such as chemical molecular weights for a series of stoichiometry problems.

Include files can be nested.

initval

Syntax	`$ initval = <value>`
Default	1
Function	Provides an alternative way to initialize the starting value for a variable.
Description	To start the solution procedure, Eureka requires a starting value for every variable. If a variable is not given an explicit initialization in the problem file, it is initialized with the default value, 1.

If some variables in the equation file are not explicitly initialized in the file, and if you include *initval* in the file, Eureka will use the *initval* value to initialize those variables.

listdefault

Syntax $ listdefault = <yes or no>

Default   No

Function   Lets you override the default values for the List function.

Description If you set *listdefault* to *no*, a series of prompts appears in response to the List command. These prompts allow you to override the default values set for List.

If you set *listdefault* to *yes*, Eureka automatically plugs in the default values for list_first, list_inc, and list_num, and generates the corresponding table.

Note: list_first, list_inc, and list_num are *not* directives. See Chapter 4 under the Settings menu.

max(imize)

Syntax $ max (variable)

Default   None

Function   Maximizes the specified variable.

Description When the *max* directive is in an equation file and you select Solve, Eureka finds a maximum for the specified variable. For example, with the following in an equation file

```
y = -x^2 - 4 * x + 3
$ max (y)
```

Eureka will find the value of x that yields the maximum value of y. Without a *max* directive, Eureka solves for the roots of y: the value(s) of x that yield a zero value for y [$-2 \pm \text{sqrt}(7)$].

You can use the *max* directive only once in an equation file, and you cannot use both *max* and *min* in the same file.

maxtime

Syntax	`$ maxtime = (positive integer)`
Default	200
Function	Sets a limit, in seconds, to the amount of time Eureka spends solving an equation.
Description	When you place the *maxtime* directive in an equation file, you set a limit to the amount of time Eureka spends seeking a solution.

min(imize)

Syntax	`$ min (variable)`
Default	None
Function	Minimizes the specified variable.
Description	When you place the *min* directive in an equation file, it supersedes the Solve command (which searches for roots—zeroes—of equations). Eureka will find a minimum value for the specified variable or function rather than a solution for all variables that make equations in the file equal zero.

For example, with the following in an equation file

```
y = x^2 + 4 * x + 3
$ min (y)
```

Eureka will find the value for x that yields the minimum value of y. Without the *min* directive, Eureka would solve for those values of x which make $y = 0$ (-3 and -1).

You can use the *min* directive only once in an equation file, and you cannot use both *max* and *min* in the same file.

penalty

Syntax	`$ penalty = <any positive real>`
Default	30
Function	Sets a weight (relative importance) for the constraints affecting an equation.
Description	Eureka uses the value of *penalty* to calculate the effect of the constraints in an equation file. Changing the default affects the relative strength of the constraint criteria.

plotdefault

Syntax	`$ plotdefault = <yes or no>`
Default	No
Function	Lets you override the default values for the Plot command.
Description	If you set *plotdefault* to *no*, a series of prompts appears in response to the Plot command, allowing you to override the default values set for Plot.

If you set *plotdefault* to *yes*, Eureka automatically plugs in the default values for plot_left and plot_right, and generates the corresponding plot. The default values for plot_left and plot_right are -2 and 10, respectively.

Note: plot_left and plot_right are *not* directives. See Chapter 4, page 72 for more information.

radius

Syntax	`$ radius = <none, or any positive real number>`
Default	None
Function	Sets a limit to the range over which Eureka seeks a solution.
Description	If you set *radius* to *no*, Eureka will search an indefinite range of numbers, limited only by its internal constraints, accuracy, and the *maxtime* directive.

If you set *radius* to a real number, Eureka will only search a range of numbers that are equal to or less than the number specified.

rootsign

Syntax	`$ rootsign = <pos or neg>`
Default	Pos
Function	Toggles between displaying the roots of an even-powered number as negative or positive numbers.
Description	If you set *rootsign* to *pos*, Eureka displays roots of even powers as all positive values; if you set it to *neg*, Eureka displays the roots as all negative values.

settings

Syntax

```
$ settings
<directive>
<directive>
    .
    .
    .
$ end
```

Default None

Function Allows you to enter several directives in a series without having to set each one off with a $ symbol.

Description You can think of the *settings* directive as the first, or opening, step in a three-step process for changing multiple settings.

The second step is to type in the directives for the settings that are changing (without typing in the initial $ symbol each time).

The final step is to close the change session by typing in the *end* directive.

If you have a group of frequently used settings, you can store them in a separate file. You can then introduce this separate Settings file into an equation file with the *include* directive.

Refer to the description of the *include* directive in this chapter for more information.

solve

Syntax `$ solve (variable)`

Default All

Function Specifies which variable in an equation file Eureka will solve for.

Description By default, Eureka solves for all variables in an equation file. However, you can use the *solve* directive to tell Eureka to solve for only the designated variable and ignore the rest.

substlevel

Syntax	`$ substlevel = <0, 1, 2, 3, 4, 5, or 6>`
Default	6
Function	Sets the maximum amount of internal variable substitutions Eureka can perform when solving an equation file.
Description	The default, 6, allows Eureka to make the maximum number of substitutions during a Solve process. Substitution level 5 allows Eureka to make fewer substitutions; level 4 allows less than level 5, and so on down to substitution level 0, which allows no substitutions.

syntax

Syntax	`$ syntax = <0, 1, or 2>`
Default	0
Function	Specifies one of three possible options for the syntax of arithmetic expressions used in the equation file.
Description	There are three options for the syntax of arithmetic expressions:

0: The default syntax, which requires the * symbol to represent multiplication. The default syntax allows scientific notation.

1: Does not allow scientific notation, because a number placed before a variable is treated as a multiplier.

2: Does not allow scientific notation, for the same reason as syntax level 1. Also restricts variables to one letter each, rather than the default choice of up to 60 alphanumeric characters.

Examples of each syntax level

Syntax = 0: The default syntax is the standard used throughout this manual.

Syntax = 1: Scientific notation (such as $2.3e - 4$ to represent 0.00023) is not allowed because Eureka interprets it as $2.3 \times$ (a variable called e) $- 4$. A number before a variable name is interpreted as a multiplier.

For example, when *syntax* = 1, Eureka treats the expression

```
2.7 water
```

as an abbreviation for

```
2.7 * water
```

As when *syntax* = 0, Eureka ignores spaces. However, the program still treats a character string (such as *dog34*) as a variable name.

Syntax = 2: Variables are restricted to a single letter. All juxtapositions of numbers and variables are treated as products.

For example, a problem to find the intersection of two hyperbolas in the $x - y$ plane could be formulated as:

```
$ syntax = 2
x^2  — 4xy + 3y^2 = 7
2xy — 5y + 3 = 0
{ exact solution is x = 2, y = 3 }
```

When *syntax* = 2, variable names must be distinct from function names; otherwise, an expression such as $f(x + 1)$ is ambiguous (i.e., is f a variable multiplying $x + 1$, or is it a function of $x + 1$?).

If the equation file contains a user-defined function, the function definition must precede the first use of the function.

Refer to the section "Notes On Equation File Syntax" (page 82) for more information about writing equations using the default syntax level.

units (conversion)

Syntax	`$ units`
	`<unit1> -> <unit2> : <formula>`
	.
	.
	.
	`$ end`
Default	No automatic conversion
Function	Defines unit conversions.
Description	Eureka can automatically associate units to variables, and then convert the values of the variables to other units in the Solution window.

For example, the variable *dist* can appear in the equation file expressed in feet, but can be converted to meters and yards when Eureka solves for its value.

The *units* conversion directive lets you define as many unit conversions as needed. For example,

```
$ units
cm -> in : x/2.54
F. -> C. : (x - 32) * 5/9
feet -> yds : x/3
km/hr -> mi/hr : 0.6214 * x
$ end
```

Each line after *$ units* gives a formula for converting from one unit of measurement to another.

The first formula converts from centimeters (cm) to inches (in); x is simply a dummy variable. The formula states that if x is in centimeters, dividing x by 2.54 will convert it from centimeters to inches.

The names for the units can be any sequence of characters, including punctuation and math symbols, as long as the symbol does not include a hyphen (-) or a colon (:). Eureka ignores blanks. The syntax for expressions is the standard Eureka syntax.

You associate units with the variables in the initialization statement. For example, the initialization

```
dist := 122.7 [cm]
```

initializes the variable *dist* to 122.7 centimeters. When solving for *dist*, Eureka first gives the solution in centimeters, then converts the value in centimeters to any other units for which a *units* conversion directive exists.

Here is a typical solution for this example:

```
dist = 110.0235 cm
     = 43.3163 in
```

Eureka can invert any simple unit conversion. If the equation file contains the formula for converting from centimeters to inches, it is not necessary to also give the formula for converting from inches to centimeters.

Eureka Functions

Besides providing a wide variety of standard mathematical and special built-in functions, Eureka also allows you to define and use your own functions. Most of the built-in functions need little explanation; they are described in Appendix C. However, the financial functions require some in-depth explanation; they are discussed in detail in this chapter. After the section about financial functions in this chapter, we give an explanation of user-defined functions.

Financial Functions

Eureka has three functions for performing interest-rate calculations: *fval*, *paymt*, and *pval*.

These functions are designed for situations in which a person enters into a contract by which a fixed sum is paid at regular intervals. We assume that money earns interest at some fixed rate, with the interest compounded in each interval.

In general, there are five variables involved in these financial calculations:

n	number of payment intervals
i	interest rate per payment interval
pval	present value of the contract
paymt	payment at the end of each interval
fval	future value of the contract

Given any four of these five variables, Eureka can solve for the fifth. The variables are related by the financial functions in the following ways:

$$pval = pval(i,n,paymt,fval)$$
$$paymt = paymt(i,n,pval,fval)$$
$$fval = fval(i,n,pval,paymt)$$

n and i can be derived directly from the values of the other variables using Solve.

Variables

The number of payment intervals, n, is normally an integer, but it can be any positive number.

If n is not an integer, there is a fractional period that is assumed to occur before all other periods. Interest is compounded at the end of, but not during, the fractional period. The *finanmode* directive can place the fractional period at the beginning or end of the series.

i, the interest rate, should not be converted to a percentage rate.

For example, $i = 0.12$ if the interest rate is 12%. The interest is compounded at the end of each payment interval.

Functions

pval, paymt, and *fval* all represent money that changes hands. By convention, the number is positive for money received and negative for money paid out.

pval, the present value, is defined as the principal: the money received (loaned) at the beginning of the contract. In the case of a home mortgage, *pval* is the price of the home minus the down payment.

paymt, the payment, is the money received at the end of each payment interval. If the person pays the money out, as with a home mortgage, *paymt* is a negative amount.

fval, the future value, is the money received at the end of the contract. In the case of a home mortgage, *fval* is either zero or a negative number that represents the balloon payment.

Example

A typical use of the financial functions would be to compute the payments on a mortgage.

For example, suppose a house costs $100,000; the interest rate is 12%; and the mortgage is for a period of 30 years. Assume that the down payment is 10%, there is no balloon payment, and payments and interest compounding are monthly.

Using *paymt,* the monthly payment can be calculated as follows:

paymt(0.12/12,30 $\times$ 12,90000,0)

where 0.12/12 is the monthly interest rate, 30 $\times$ 12 is the number of payments, 90000 is the amount of principal, and 0 is no balloon.

Note: The last argument would be non-zero only if there were a balloon payment at the end of the 30 years.

By default, Eureka assumes that payments are made at the end of each interval rather than at the beginning. This is because the settings parameter *finanmode* has the following default value:

```
finanmode = end
```

You can change this setting to *begin* either from the Options/Settings pull-down menu or by directive in the equation file.

Because banks often have their own unique methods for computing interest rates, Eureka's built-in financial functions may vary slightly from any particular bank's methods.

User-defined Functions

Eureka deals primarily with variables and the relationships among them. It is often convenient to think of variables as functions of one another, and Eureka does so with its set of built-in functions.

You can add to Eureka's set of functions by defining your own for a given equation file; these are known as *user-defined functions*. The following discussion describes the relationship between variables and functions and then explains various aspects of user-defined functions.

Relationship of Variables and Functions in Eureka

Consider an equation with one or more variables in which it is possible to solve for one variable in terms of the others. This solved variable could, in effect, be expressed as a function of the other variables. However, to Eureka, it is still just a variable.

For example, the function $\sin(x) + \cos(x)$ can be maximized by maximizing f where

$$f = \sin(x) + \cos(x)$$

Here, f can be conceived as a variable that happens to be related to x.

In another example, the equation

$$x^2 + y^2 = 25$$

might be transformed by Eureka internally to either

$$x = \text{sqrt}(25 - y^2)$$

or

$$y = \text{sqrt}(25 - x^2)$$

In other words, x can be considered as a function of y, or y as a function of x. To a user, however, x and y are simply related variables.

Eureka recognizes two types of functions:

- built-in functions (such as *cos* and *sin*)
- user-defined functions

Built-in functions have no values unless arguments are supplied, and it makes no sense for Eureka to solve for them.

User-defined functions describe configurations of variables that you wish to capture in shorthand fashion.

Note: User-defined functions affect only the equation files in which they are defined.

Writing User-defined Functions

The symbol := flags a user-defined function as in

```
trig(x) := sin(x) + cos(x)
```

This example defines a new function called *trig* that acts in the same way as a built-in function. The variable x is a dummy variable that merely serves to define the function and is unrelated to any other x that may occur elsewhere in the equation file.

When an equation file contains this user-defined function, trig(x), you can insert

```
trig(7)
```

or

```
trig(a * b + 3)
```

into an equation rather than inserting the lengthier expressions

```
(sin(7) + cos(7))
```

or

```
(sin(a * b + 3) + cos(a * b + 3))
```

The lexical rules regarding function names are the same as those for variable names (begin with a letter or certain special characters, limited to 60 alphanumeric characters). Although you can give the same name to a variable and a function, this practice is not recommended. You can define a function of several variables (or even no variables).

For instance, defining a function by

```
gas(x,y) := x + y * z + 10
```

causes the expression $2 * \text{gas}(3, a + 1)$ to be treated as

```
2 * (3 + (a + 1) * z + 10)
```

For most equation solving purposes, user-defined functions are essentially editing conveniences. However, several Eureka features require user-defined functions:

- making plots or tables
- finding roots of polynomials
- solving differential calculus problems

Error Messages

When writing user-defined functions, keep in mind that Eureka returns an error if:

1. You use a function without defining it somewhere in the equation file.

2. You redefine a function in the equation file.

3. A function calls for a certain number of arguments, but you use it with a different number of arguments than those defined, as in

   ```
   f(x,y,z) := x^2 - y^2 + z^2
   f(a,b) = 100
   ```

4. You define a function in a circular way, as in

   ```
   f(x) := x^2 + 3 * g(x)
   g(x) := f(x + 1) - 7 * x
   ```

Eureka: The Solver Owner's Handbook

Worked Examples

This chapter provides several worked problems. These examples are designed to demonstrate Eureka's power in solving a variety of mathematical problems. The problems are contained on your distribution disk under the following file names:

Problem 1 Quick Demo	CLASSICS.EKA, DERINT.EKA, MAXMIN.EKA, COMPLEX.EKA
Problem 2 Loan Payoff	CARLOAN.EKA
Problem 3 Ladders in an Alley	LADDERS.EKA
Problem 4 Distribution of Line Charges	LINECHG.EKA
Problem 5 Radioactive Decay	DECAY.EKA
Problem 6 Least-Squares Fit	LSQRFIT.EKA
Problem 7 Motion of a Projectile	PROJCTL.EKA
Problem 8 Charged Masses	MASSCHG.EKA
Problem 9 Using the *Poly* Function	POLYNOM.EKA
Problem 10 Maximization (House Design)	HOUSE.EKA
Problem 11 Maximization (Linear Program)	LINPROG.EKA
Problem 12 Equity in a House	EQUITY.EKA
Problem 13 Probability in a Card Game	CARDS.EKA

Problem 14 Income Distribution (Integ Function) INTEG.EKA
Problem 15 Chemical Calculations CHEMBAL.EKA,
CHEMEQ1.EKA,
CHEMEQ2.EKA,
CHEMEQ3.EKA

The first series of problems demonstrate Eureka's basic features:

- solving systems of nonlinear (and linear) equations
- solving and plotting user-defined functions
- calculating a least-squares fit
- solving transcendental functions

Later problems incorporate some of Eureka's special capabilities and built-in functions:

- maximizations and minimizations
- definite integrals
- factorials
- polynomial solutions
- financial calculations

If you want to get an idea of how to set up and solve problems with Eureka, or if you want to see how we have incorporated some of Eureka's capabilities and features into an assortment of problems, we suggest you look over and study some or all of the examples in this chapter. They include a sampling from a variety of fields and topics: chemistry, finance, probability, physics, electrostatics, and economics, to name a few.

Each worked problem consists of:

- a statement of the problem
- an explanation of the model equations
- a copy of the report generated after Eureka solves the problem

All of the reports contain the equation file and the contents of Eureka's Solution window for the problem. Some reports also include the contents of Eureka's Verify window, comparing the solution values with the original equations and constraints. Other reports include a two-column table (generated with Eureka's Graph/List command) that compares values of a specified function from the equation file with the function variable.

Remember—Eureka: The Solver is designed to help you solve a whole world of mathematical problems: This chapter presents but a small sample of what Eureka can do!

Problem 1
A Quick Demonstration of Eureka's
Mathematical Capabilities

This problem (CLASSICS.EKA, DERINT.EKA, MAXMIN.EKA, and COM-PLEX.EKA on the distribution disk) highlights some of Eureka's capabilities. It demonstrates how Eureka:

- quickly solves basic mathematical identities
- calculates and plots definite integrals and derivatives
- solves integral problems
- maximizes or minimizes functions over a given range
- solves for complex variables

This example is broken into four sets of problems, covering four topics:

- classic identities
- integrals and derivatives
- minimizations and maximizations
- complex variables

In the first set of problems, Classic Identities, Eureka solves a few trigonometric and transcendental equations. You already know the solutions to the equations; our purpose in demonstrating how Eureka handles them is to familiarize you with how fast (and how well) the equation solver works.

The second set of problems, Derivatives and Integrals, illustrates how you use Eureka's built-in *integ* and *deriv* functions, and shows how to set up user-defined functions (delimited with the := symbol) so Eureka can plot them.

Maximizations and Minimizations, the third set of problems, demonstrates how to incorporate Eureka's *max* and *min* directives in your equation files. Maximizations (and minimizations) are not an easy task for a computer program, especially when the variables are subject to certain constraints. However, as you will see in this set of problems, Eureka solves them with ease.

The final set of problems, Complex Variables, shows how Eureka solves for both the real (re) and imaginary (im) part of problems such as

$$y^2 + 1 = 0 \text{ and } e^{i \times \mathrm{pi}} = theta.$$

Statement of the Problem

Suppose you were given the following (admittedly simple) problems to solve with a hand-held calculator. How long would it take you to solve for the given variables, verify that your answers were appropriate, and plot the functions requested?

Classic Identities

1. Solve for x where $\ln(x) = 1$; plot the function for $0.1 < x < 5$

2. Solve for y where $\sin(y/2) = 1$

3. Solve for z where $\tan(z/4) = 1$

4. Plot $F(a) = \sin(a)/a$ for $-10 < a < 10$
    Solve for j where $F(j) = 1/2$

Derivatives and Integrals

5. Given the following functions A, B, C, and D:
    $A(x) = (\cos(x))^2$
    $B(x) = \sin(x)$
    $C(x) = \cos(x/2)$
    $D(x) = A(x) + B(x) + C(x)$

    a. Plot $D(x)$ for $-10 < x < 10$

    b. Calculate the integral of $A(x)$ for $0 < x < 5$

    c. Calculate the integral of $D(x)$ for $0 < x < 5$

    d. Find a zero of $dA(x)/dx$

    e. Find a zero of $dB(x)/dx$

    f. Find a zero of $dC(x)/dx$

    g. Find two zeroes of $dD(x)/dx$: one negative, one non-negative

Maximizations and Minimizations

6. For the function $F(a)$ in problem 4:

    a. Find the minimum value of $F(a)$ over the range $0.1 < a < 10$

    b. Find the maximum value of $F(a)$ over the range $-10 < a < -4$

7. At what point $x > 0$ does the integral of [sin(a) da] reach the value 1?

8. Maximization: at what point $x > 0$ does the integral of [sin(a) da] reach a maximum value?

9. Maximization: at what point c on the range -4 to 4 does sin(c) reach a maximum?

10. Minimization: at what point a on the range -4 to 4 does sin(a) reach a minimum?

11. Plot sin(a) over the range $-4 < a < 4$

Complex Variables

12. Solve for the variables x, y, and *theta* in the following equations:

$$x^2 = -1$$
$$y^2 + 1 = 0$$
$$\exp(x \times \text{pi}) = theta \ (\text{pi} = 3.1415926)$$

Would you look forward to solving, evaluating and plotting these functions with only the aid of a calculator and a pencil? Probably not.

Not only can Eureka solve for the given variables; the equation solver can also plot the requested functions and evaluate the solutions (flagging any that don't satisfy the given constraints). Not only that, Eureka will generate complete, formatted written reports giving the original problems, the solutions, the evaluations and the plots. And you never have to lift a pencil.

Equations

___

For the given problems, Eureka will solve these corresponding equations:

1. $L(x) := \ln(x)$
   $L(A) = 1.00000$

2. $S(x) := \sin(x/2.0)$
   $S(B) = 1.00000$

3. $T(x) := \tan(x/4.0)$
   $T(C) = 1.00000$

4. $F(x) := \sin(x)/x$
   $F(j1) = 0.50000 : j1 < 0$
   $F(j2) = 0.50000 : j2 > 0$

5. $A(x) := (\cos(x))^2$
       $B(x) := \sin(x)$
       $C(x) := \cos(x/2)$

       $D(x) := A(x) + B(x) + C(x)$
       $D(dd1) = 0 : 0 < dd1 < 10$
       $D(dd2) = 0 : dd2 := -1$

       $Ap(x) := \text{deriv}((\cos(x))^2, x)$
       $Bp(x) := \text{deriv}(\sin(x), x)$
       $Cp(x) := \text{deriv}(\cos(x/2), x)$
       $Dp(x) := \text{deriv}(D(x), x)$

       $Ap(ap) = 0$
       $Bp(bp) = 0$
       $Cp(cp) = 0$
       $Dp(dp) = 0$

       $Dintl = \text{integ}(D(x), x, 0, 5)$
       $Aintl = \text{integ}(A(x), x, 0, 5)$

      Eureka will solve for *ap, bp, cp, dp, dd1, dd2, Aintl*, and *Dintl*. Those equations containing the := symbol are "user-defined" functions; refer to Chapter 5 for more information about these and other special Eureka functions.

6. $F(z) := \sin(z)/z$

       \$ min (K)
       $K = F(z)$
       $0.1 < z < 10$

       \$ max (L)
       $L = F(z)$
       $-10 < z < -4$

7. $1.000 = \text{integ}(\sin(a), a, 0, w/2)$
       $w/2 = x$

8.   \$ max (I)
       $I = \text{MaxInt}(x)$
       $\text{MaxInt}(a) := \text{integ}(\sin(a), a, 0, x)$

9.   \$ max (z)
       $z = S(c)$
       $S(c) := \sin(c)$
       $-4 < c < 4$
       $d = 2c$

10.   \$ min (y)
       $y = S(a)$
       $S(a) := \sin(a)$

$$-4 < a < 4$$
$$b = 2a$$

11. $S(a) := \sin(a)$

12. $x^2 = -1$
$$y^2 + 1 = 0$$
$$\exp(x \times \text{pi}) = \textit{theta} : \text{pi} = 3.1415926$$

To solve these problems, select one of the equation files (use File/Load from the main menu), then select Solve.

Equation Files and Solutions

The print-outs that follow show the equation files and Eureka's solutions for the examples in this problem.

Graphing the Functions

Eureka also offers the ability to plot functions of one variable. To graph any one of the functions in these problems:

- Solve the equation file.
- Select the Graph option from the main menu.
- From the Graph menu, choose Plot.
- Select one function from the mini-menu listing of all user-defined functions.
- Enter values for the left and right x axis endpoints.

Eureka will automatically plot the function.

Generating Reports

You can also direct Eureka to generate your own written reports; after solving an equation file (also evaluating the solutions, if you choose) and plotting a function, select Report from the main menu. Eureka will place the report on screen, write it to a disk file, or send it directly to your printer, as you choose.

Note: We used Borland's SideKick to capture the "zoomed" plots and insert them in the reports that follow.

```
*******************************************************************
Eureka: The Solver, Version 1.0
Thursday February 12, 1987, 10:13 am.
Name of input file: CLASSICS.EKA
*******************************************************************


; These examples show how Eureka quickly
; solves some classic problems

L(x) := ln(x)
L(A) = 1.00000
;  plot L(x) for 0.1 < x < 5

S(x) := sin(x/2.0)
S(B) = 1.00000

T(x) := tan(x/4.0)
T(C) = 1.00000

; After solving this equation file, plot
; the function F(x) for -10 < x < 10

F(x) := sin(x)/x
F(j1) = 0.50000 : j1 < 0
F(j2) = 0.50000 : j2 > 0

*******************************************************************

Solution:

Variables    Values

A         =    2.7182818

B         =    3.1524423

C         =    3.1416042

j1        =   -1.8954943

j2        =    1.8954943

Maximum error is .000014714291

***********************************************************************
```

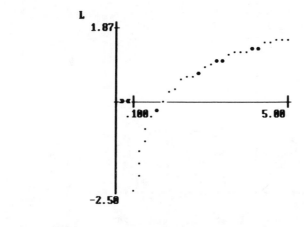

```
L
1.87
```

```
.100.          5.00
```

```
-2.50
```

****

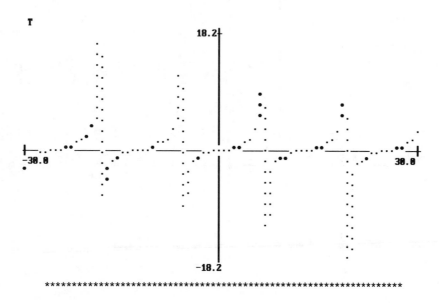

```
T                    18.2
```

```
-30.0                              30.0
```

```
-18.2
```

****

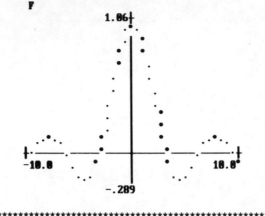

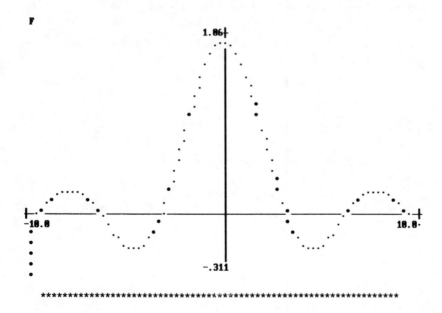

```
*******************************************************************
Eureka: The Solver, Version 1.0
Thursday February 12, 1987, 11:23 am.
Name of input file: DERINT.EKA
*******************************************************************

; These problems demonstrate how to use
; Eureka's INTEG and DERIV functions, and
; include examples of plotting the
; functions

A(x) := (cos(x))^2
B(x) := sin(x)
C(x) := cos(x/2)

D(x) := A(x) + B(x) + C(x)
D(dd1) = 0 : 0 < dd1 < 10
D(dd2) = 0 : dd2 := -1

Ap(x) := deriv((cos(x))^2, x)
Bp(x) := deriv(sin(x), x)
Cp(x) := deriv(cos(x/2), x)
Dp(x) := deriv(D(x), x)

Ap(ap) = 0
Bp(bp) = 0
Cp(cp) = 0
Dp(dp) = 0

Dintl = integ(D(x),x,0,5)
Aintl = integ(A(x),x,0,5)


*******************************************************************

Solution:

Variables    Values

Aintl    =      2.3639947

ap       =      1.5707964

bp       =      1.5707964

cp       =   -1.8097622e-10

dd1      =      3.6612084

dd2      =     -2.2077911

Dintl    =      4.2772768

dp       =     -349.75174

Maximum error is    .067092381
```

```
******************************************************************

Evaluation of formulas:

Formulas          Values

D(dd1)            = -6.1014156e-08
0                 =     .00000000
 difference (error) = -6.1014156e-08


0                 =     .00000000
dd1               =    3.6612084
 difference =    -3.6612084


10                =    10.000000
dd1               =    3.6612084
 difference =    -6.3387916


D(dd2)            = 4.0720587e-08
0                 =     .00000000
 difference (error) = 4.0720587e-08


dd2               =    -2.2077911


Ap(ap)            = 8.7422780e-08
0                 =     .00000000
 difference (error) = 8.7422780e-08


Bp(bp)            = -4.3711390e-08
0                 =     .00000000
 difference (error) = -4.3711390e-08


Cp(cp)            = 4.5244055e-11
0                 =     .00000000
 difference (error) = 4.5244055e-11


Dp(dp)            =   -.067092381
0                 =     .00000000
 difference (error) =   -.067092381


Dintl             =    4.2772768
integ(D(x),x... =    4.2772768
 difference =     .00000000


Aintl             =    2.3639947
integ(A(x),x... =    2.3639947
 difference =     .00000000

Maximum error is   .067092381
```

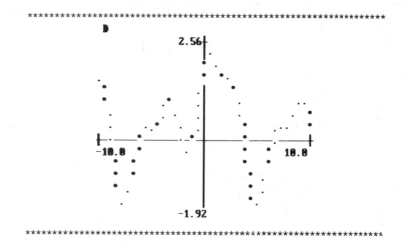

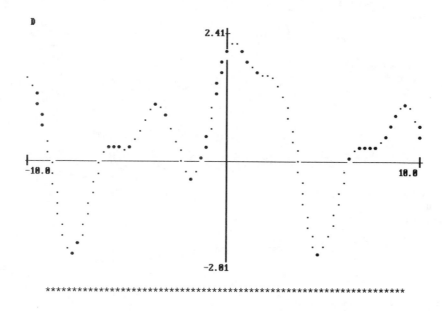

```
******************************************************************
Eureka: The Solver, Version 1.0
Thursday February 12, 1987, 11:48 am.
Name of input file: MAXMIN.EKA
******************************************************************
```

; These examples illustrate how to use
; Eureka's $max and $min directives to
; maximize and minimize any variable that
; is defined to be the result of a given
; function. One of these examples also
; demonstrates how to solve an integral
; equation with Eureka.

; NOTE: To solve any one of these examples,
; remove the ";" symbol at the beginning of
; each equation line for that example.
; Eureka will only solve for ONE $min or
; $max in an equation file. To solve a
; different example, first reinsert the ";"
; symbols from the previously-solved
; example.

; Part 1: A well-known example:
; F(z) := sin(z)/z

; Problem 1-a:
; $min (K)
; K = F(z)
; 0.1 < z < 10

; Problem 1-b:
; $ max (L)
; L = F(z)
; -10 < z < -4

; Part 2: Integral of Sin(x) dx

; Problem 2-a:
; Solving an integral equation: at what
; point x > 0 does the integral of
; [sin(a) da] reach the value 1?
; (Let w/2 equal x.)

; 1.000 = integ(sin(a), a, 0, w/2)
; w/2 = x

; Problem 2-b:
; Maximization: at what point x > 0 does
; the integral of [sin(a) da] reach a
; maximum value?

; $max (I)
; I = MaxInt(a)
; MaxInt(a) := integ(sin(a), a, 0, x)

; Part 3: Max and Min of Sin(x)

```
; Problem 3-a:
; Maximization: at what point c on the
; range -4 to 4 does sin(c) reach a
; maximum? (Note: The function S(c) is
; included for plotting purposes - Eureka
; does not need it to solve for c or z.)

; $max (z)
; z = S(c)
; S(c) := sin(c)
; -4 < c < 4
; d = 2*c

; Problem 3-b:
; Minimization: at what point a on the
; range -4 to 4 does sin(a) reach a
; minimum? (Note: The function S(a) is
; included for plotting purposes - Eureka
; does not need it to solve for a or y.)

; $min (y)
; y = S(a)
; S(a) := sin(a)
; -4 < a < 4
; b = 2*a
```

****

Solution: (1-a)

Variables   Values

K   =   -.21723363

z   =   4.4934066

Confidence level =   98.9%
All constraints satisfied.

****

****

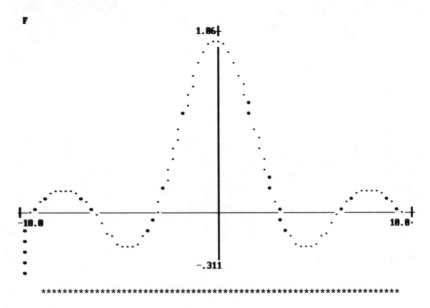

```
*********************************************************************

Solution: (2-a)

Variables    Values

w         =     3.1415882

x         =     1.5707941

Maximum error is 2.2415074e-06


*********************************************************************

Evaluation of formulas:

Formulas          Values

1.000           =     1.0000000
integ(sin(a)... =      .99999776
 difference (error) = 2.2415074e-06


w/2             =     1.5707941
x               =     1.5707941
 difference =      .00000000

Maximum error is 2.2415074e-06

*********************************************************************
```

```
Solution: (2-b)

Variables    Values

I        =    2.0000000

x        =    3.1415927

Confidence level =   100.0%
All constraints satisfied.

*********************************************************************

Solution: (3-a)

Variables    Values

c        =    1.5707963

d        =    3.1415927

z        =    1.0000000

Confidence level =    98.7%
All constraints satisfied.

*********************************************************************
```

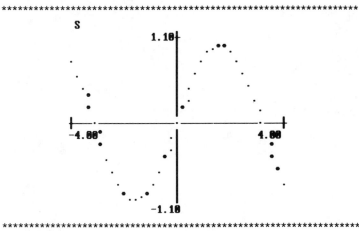

```
*********************************************************************

Solution: (3-b)

Variables    Values

a        =    -1.5707963

b        =    -3.1415926

y        =    -1.00000000

Confidence level =    98.7%
All constraints satisfied.

*********************************************************************
```

```
********************************************************************
Eureka: The Solver, Version 1.0
Thursday February 12, 1987, 1:35 pm.
Name of input file: COMPLEX.EKA
********************************************************************

; This example demonstrates how Eureka
; solves for complex variables

$ complex = yes

x^2 = -1
y^2 + 1 = 0

exp(x*pi) = theta
pi = 3.1415926


********************************************************************

Solution:

Variables    Values

re pi     =      3.1415926
im pi     =      .00000000

re theta  =    -1.00000000
im theta  = 5.3589793e-08

re x      = 6.1257423e-17
im x      =      1.0000000

re y      = 1.0783729e-27
im y      =      1.0000000
********************************************************************
```

Problem 2
Loan Payoff

This problem (CARLOAN.EKA on the distribution disk) demonstrates how to set up equations for a financing situation and use Eureka's Graph/List capability to generate a list of function values *vs.* the variable, *time.*

Statement of the Problem

The car you purchased cost $10,900. When you bought it, you made a down payment of $2,900 and financed the rest ($8,000) for 48 months at 13.5% annually. Now it is a year and a half later, and you are thinking about buying a new car.

- How much would it cost to pay off the loan?
- How long should you continue to make payments?

These questions can be answered by a few mathematical calculations. To start with, define some terms:

Pay = periodic payment
Int = interest per period
Prin = principal amount borrowed
ntot = the total number of periods for the original loan
n = the number of periods actually paid before payoff
FofP = the future value of the principal at month *n*, given a present value
FofA = the future value of a payment series at month *n*, given a periodic payment

Using these terms, you first need to calculate the original payment. You could use the built-in function *paymt*, but this time you are going to use the actual mathematical formula to see how it is done.

Once you know the monthly payment, you need to find the remainder of the principal at a given month, then subtract the value of the sum of remaining payments.

To do this, use the time at which you borrowed the money as a reference point. From this point, find the future value of the principal (*FofP*) at the time of the payoff and the future value of the payment series (*FofA*) at the time of the payoff. After subtracting *FofA* from *FofP*, you have the payoff amount.

By making the formula for *PayOff* a function of *n*, you can generate a list of 20 possible payoff points with the Eureka Graph/List function. This can help you make your decision.

Equations

The first step when setting up the equations for this problem is to define the variables and assign values to them. The variables are:

Monthly interest (*IntM*) is 13.5 annual percentage rate divided by 12 months per year:

$$IntM = (13.5/100)/12 = 0.01125$$

Principal, the amount borrowed:

$$Prin = 8,000.00$$

Total number of payments for the loan:

$$ntot = 48$$

Monthly payment (to be calculated from given variables):

PayM

The equations required for solving the two questions posed by this problem are:

Calculate the monthly payment:

$$PayM = Prin \times IntM \times ((1 + IntM)^{ntot - 1})/((1 + IntM) - 1)$$

Calculate the future value of the original loan amount at the specified time *n*, where *n* indicates one of the 48 months:

$$FofP(n) := (Prin \times (1 + IntM)^n)$$

Calculate the future value of the payments at the same specified month, *n*:

$$FofA(n) = (PayM \times ((1 + IntM)^n - 1)/IntM)$$

(Note that these two calculations are made from user-defined functions.)

Finally, for a given month, *n*, calculate the *Payoff*: What is the principal that remains outstanding after the payment *n*?

$$PayOff(n) := FofP(n) - FofA(n)$$

Equation File and Solution

The equation file and solution for this problem appear in the print-out that follows, along with the table generated using Eureka's Graph/List command. The table lists the function, *Payoff*, vs. months 15 through 34.

```
********************************************************************
Eureka: The Solver, Version 1.0
Thursday November 6, 1986, 5:47 am.
Name of input file: CARLOAN.EKA
********************************************************************

$  finansmooth = yes

IntM = .01125
Prin = 8000.00
ntot = 48
n = (1+IntM)^ntot

PayM = Prin * IntM * ((1+IntM)^ntot) / ((1+IntM)^ntot - 1)
FofP(n) := (Prin * (1+IntM)^n)
FofA(n) := (PayM * ((1+IntM)^n - 1) / IntM)
PayOff(n) :=  FofP(n) - FofA(n)

********************************************************************

Solution:

Variables    Values

IntM      =    .011250000

ntot      =    48.000000

PayM      =    216.61058

Prin      =    8000.0000

n         =    1.7108410


********************************************************************
```

List of function values.

n	PayOff(n)
15.000000	5943.7392
16.000000	5793.9957
17.000000	5642.5676
18.000000	5489.4359
19.000000	5334.5814
20.000000	5177.9849
21.000000	5019.6267
22.000000	4859.4869
23.000000	4697.5455
24.000000	4533.7823
25.000000	4368.1768
26.000000	4200.7082
27.000000	4031.3556
28.000000	3860.0977
29.000000	3686.9133
30.000000	3511.7804
31.000000	3334.6774
32.000000	3155.5819
33.000000	2974.4716
34.000000	2791.3239

****

Problem 3
Ladders in an Alley: Solving Simultaneous Nonlinear Equations

This problem (LADDERS.EKA on the distribution disk) demonstrates Eureka's ability to quickly and accurately solve simultaneous nonlinear equations.

Statement of the Problem

You have two ladders, one 35 feet long, the other 45 feet long. You need to arrange them in an alley between two skyscrapers so that they cross 10 feet above the ground. How wide should the alley be?

Equations

First, assign variables to all the known and desired quantities:

x = width of the alley
a = height of the 45-foot ladder at the wall
b = height of the 35-foot ladder at the wall
h = the point on the ground immediately below where the ladders meet.

Equation File and Solution

The print-out that follows shows the equation file and solution for this problem.

Notice the initialization values for the four variables. If you have a general idea about the region where the solution(s) lie, it's a good idea to start Eureka off within or close to that region. Eureka solves problems such as this one by iteration, getting closer and closer to an error-free solution. However, the default value for all initializations is 1.

When you are confident that the solution(s) are significantly larger (or smaller) than 1, you can initialize the variables with some plausible values, then tell Eureka to Solve. This way, Eureka will not spend a lot of time covering unproductive ground.

When you are confident that the solution(s) are significantly larger (or smaller) than 1, you can initialize the variables with some plausible values, then tell Eureka to Solve. This way, Eureka will not spend a lot of time covering unproductive ground.

If Eureka's first round of iterations produces an unsatisfactory solution, you can use other techniques to get the program re-solving in a different region. These other techniques are covered in Chapters 3 and 5 of this manual.

```
********************************************************************
Eureka: The Solver, Version 1.0
Thursday November 6, 1986, 6:47 am.
Name of input file: LADDERS.EKA
********************************************************************


; This example demonstrates how Eureka can solve
; a system of nonlinear equations iteratively, after
; you initialize the iteration.

; System of nonlinear equations:

    x^2 + a^2 = 45^2
    x^2 + b^2 = 35^2
    y/10 = x/b
    (x-y)/10 = x/a

; Initializations:
    x := 10
    y := 10
    a := 20
    b := 20

; constraints:
    a>0
    b>0
    x>0
    x>y
    y>0

; Exact solutions are: x = 31.817459 , y = 21.818934
; and a = 31.822151 , b = 14.582500

********************************************************************

Solution:

Variables    Values

a       =    31.822151

b       =    14.582500

x       =    31.817459

y       =    21.818934


Maximum error is 6.8212103e-13

********************************************************************
```

Problem 4
Distribution of Line Charges

This problem in electrostatics (LINECHG.EKA on the distribution disk) illustrates Eureka's ability to solve several simultaneous nonlinear equations.

Statement of the Problem

A system of several parallel positive line charges is aligned along an axis within an electric field so that the total force exerted on each line charge is zero.

As shown in Figure 6-1, a line charge is fixed at the origin, lying on the z axis. Three free-line charges lie on the $x - z$ plane (positive x) parallel to the first. The electric field is constant in magnitude and aligned in the negative x direction. From physics, you know that the force on a charge is proportional to the electric field and like charges repel.

The problem is to distribute the line charges along the x axis so that the sum of forces on each of the three free charges equals zero.

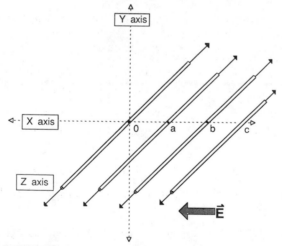

Figure 6-1 Line Charges in Equilibrium

This problem requires you to solve a set of nonlinear equations. (An interesting note: The same equations which govern this problem also apply to the distribution of dislocations under uniform shear stress in the study of the fracture of solids.)

Equations

From basic electrostatic theory, you know that the electric field produced by a line charge varies

- inversely with the first power of the distance from the line, and
- linearly with the charge density of the line

The field produced by a line charge at some point p (or infinitesimal length p) has the form

$$E(\text{linecharge}) = 2l/r$$

where

l = charge density along the line (assumed to be invariant)

and

r = distance from point p to the line

The force F from a line charge at point p is the field at p multiplied by the probe's line charge density:

$$F = 2l/r \times l$$

In this example, you have an array of line charges. Each line charge produces a field that affects all its neighbors; the line charge, in turn, is affected by all its neighbors and the constant field, $E(\text{constant})$.

The force acting on any of the movable lines, Fi, is the sum of each other line's individual force acting on that line (where $Xi - Xj = r(i - j)$):

$$Fa = l \times Ea(l) = l \times (2l/r(a - 0) + 2l/r(a - b) + 2l/r(a - c))$$
$$Fb = l \times Eb(l) = l \times (2l/r(b - 0) + 2l/r(b - a) + 2l/r(b - c))$$
$$Fc = l \times Ec(l) = l \times (2l/r(c - 0) + 2l/r(c - a) + 2l/r(c - b))$$
$$Fi = (\text{sum } [j \text{ ne } i, 0 \leq j \leq 3] \ 2l^2/(X_i - X_j)) - E(\text{constant}) \times l$$

for each infinitesimal length of the line (assuming each line has the same charge density, l).

To find the solution to this problem, derive a set of coupled equations that must be solved if the force on each line charge is zero. Using the notation in Figure 6-1, derive the following equations:

$$1/(a - b) + 1/(a - c) + 1/a = E(\text{constant})/l^2$$
$$1/(b - a) + 1/(b - c) + 1/b = E(\text{constant})/l^2$$
$$1/(c - a) + 1/(c - b) + 1/c = E(\text{constant})/l^2$$

For simplicity, select values for $E(\text{constant})$ and l such that $E(\text{constant})/l^2 = 1$, then solve the resulting set of equations.

The print-out that follows shows the equation file and solution for this problem.

Notice that although Eureka generates solutions for a, b, and c, the order of the variables is not the same in the solution as it is in the equation file. This is because the equations are symmetrical with respect to interchange of the variables, and Eureka's solution process happens to produce the given order.

```
*******************************************************************
Eureka: The Solver, Version 1.0
Saturday November 8, 1986, 1:28 pm.
Name of input file: LINECHG.EKA
*******************************************************************


; This example demonstrates Eureka's ability to solve
; a system of nonlinear equations.  These equations
; represent the net force on each line charge in a
; system of 4 parallel, coplanar line charges aligned in
; an electric field.

    1/(a-b) + 1/(a-c) + 1/a  = 1

    1/(b-a) + 1/(b-c) + 1/b  = 1

    1/(c-a) + 1/(c-b) + 1/c  = 1
*******************************************************************

Solution:

Variables    Values

a        =    3.8793852

b        =     .46791111

c        =    1.6527036


Maximum error is -1.1102230e-15

*******************************************************************
```

Problem 5
Radioactive Decay

In this problem (DECAY.EKA on the distribution disk), you use Eureka to solve a transcendental function of time.

Statement of the Problem

Radioactive elements, such as uranium, decay according to an exponential law. This means that the rate of decay is constant and proportional to the amount of the material.

In the case of uranium-238, a given amount of uranium will decay into lighter elements at a rate such that half of it will have decayed every 10 million years. If 100 kilograms of uranium-238 sits for 10 million years, at the end of that period only 50 kilograms of radioactive material will remain. At the end of another 10 million years, 25 kilograms of radioactive uranium will be left.

This time period for the uranium to be reduced to half its original amount is called the *half-life*. Given 100 kilograms of uranium-238, how much radioactive material will remain after 1,000,000 years?

Equations

The rate of mass decrease as a function of time is proportional to the mass of radioactive substance at that time. Symbolically, in terms of differential calculus,

$$dm/dt = -km$$

where

m = mass
t = time
k = proportionality constant

According to the laws of calculus, the only functions to satisfy this formula are of the form $m = a \times \exp(-kt)$ where a is some constant. *HalfLife* and k are related by the formula

$$k = \ln(2)/HalfLife$$

Mathematically, the following formula gives the amount of a radioactive substance at any particular time:

$$Mass(time) = InitMass \times 2^{(-time/HalfLife)}$$

where

InitMass = initial mass (or weight) of the substance
Mass(years) = mass of the substance after a given time; in this case, years
HalfLife = half-life of the substance

Equation File and Solution

The print-out that follows shows the equation file and solution for this problem.

Because a user-defined function is entered for mass as a function of years, you can use Eureka's Graph/List capability to generate a list of the remaining radioactive mass *vs.* time. This list, covering the period from 500,000 to 5,250,000 years elapsed in increments of 250,000 years, completes the print-out.

```
********************************************************************
Eureka: The Solver, Version 1.0
Wednesday January 28, 1987, 11:30 am.
Name of input file: DECAY.EKA
********************************************************************
```

; This problem demonstrates how to solve a user-defined
; transcendental function of time.
; The problem is to calculate MassUnknwn, the mass of
; 100 kg Uranium 238 after one million years.

```
    Mass(Years) := InitMass * 2 ^ ( - Years / HalfLife)
    InitMass = 100
    HalfLife = 10 * 1e6
    MassUnknwn = Mass(1e6)
```

```
********************************************************************
```

Solution:

Variables   Values

HalfLife   =   10000000.

InitialMass =   100.00000

MassUnknwn =   93.303299

List of function values.
Mass

x	Mass(x)
500000.00	96.593633
750000.00	94.934212
1000000.0	93.303299
1250000.0	91.700404
1500000.0	90.125046
1750000.0	88.576752
2000000.0	87.055056
2250000.0	85.559503
2500000.0	84.089642
2750000.0	82.645032
3000000.0	81.225240
3250000.0	79.829839
3500000.0	78.458410
3750000.0	77.110541
4000000.0	75.785828
4250000.0	74.483873
4500000.0	73.204285
4750000.0	71.946679
5000000.0	70.710678
5250000.0	69.495911

```
********************************************************************
```

Problem 6
Least-Squares Fit

This problem (LSQRFIT.EKA on the distribution disk) demonstrates how you can direct Eureka to find values for the constants in a function so that the function closely fits predetermined data points. You do this by limiting the program's substitution level (using the *substlevel* directive) during a Solve.

Statement of the Problem

You have a set of points (x,y) from empirical data, and you know that the data ideally should fit a curve of the form

$$y = f(x) = e^{(Ax^N + B)}$$

where A, B and N are constants. You need to determine those values for A, B, and N that produce the best-fit curve for your data.

The data points are:

x_n	y_n
1	1.49
2	2.35
3	4.26
4	8.59
5	19.80

Equations

Normally, in the process of solving a problem, Eureka makes symbolic substitutions in the equation file. However, you can limit the number of times the program will substitute for terms in the file by adding a *substlevel* directive to the file. Setting *substlevel* to 0 directs Eureka to make no substitutions; this is the technique you will use here.

In this problem, you need to tell Eureka three things:

- the general form of the equation
- the data points (x,y)
- the level of substitution (none)

This user-defined function represents the general form of the equation:

$$f(x) = \exp(Ax^N + B)$$

These equations give Eureka the empirical data points with the y values given as functions of x:

$$f(1) = 1.49$$
$$f(2) = 2.35$$
$$f(3) = 4.26$$
$$f(4) = 8.59$$
$$f(5) = 19.80$$

This directive sets the level of substitution to zero:

```
$ substlevel = 0
```

For Eureka to successfully find a unique solution for the problem, the number of equations (data points) must equal or exceed the number of unknown constants in the user-defined equation. Notice that there are five equations ($f(1), f(2), f(3), f(4)$, and $f(5)$) in this problem and three unknowns (A, B, and N).

If you do not set the substitution level to zero, Eureka will solve for those values of the three unknowns (A, B and N) which satisfy the first three equations ($f(1) = 1.49, f(2) = 2.35$, and $f(3) = 4.26$) without looking at the equations for $f(4)$ and $f(5)$.

With the substitution level at zero, Eureka looks at all the given equations ($f(x) = y$) and automatically minimizes the least-squares function F where

$$F(x,y) = ((f(x_1) - y_1)^2 + (f(x_2) - y_2)^2 + (f(x_3) - y_3)^2 + (f(x_4) - y_4)^2 + (f(x_5) - y_5)^2)$$

This function, F, represents the sum of the vertical (ordinate) distances of the points (x_n, y_n) from the points $(x(n), f(x(n)))$ on the plot of the sought function. Minimizing this sum is equivalent to finding the best-fitting curve to match the plotted data.

You could enter up to 20 data points into a problem of this type, although the computations involved would make the Solve process quite lengthy. Ten data points (or less, where possible) is a more practical limit.

Additional Techniques: Inputting Data From Another Program

This is the type of problem where you can make good use of Eureka's ability to solve problems created in another software environment. For example, if you have a Turbo Basic program that generates the points x_n, y_n used in this problem and those point values are stored in two arrays, $X(I)$ and $Y(I)$, you can write a Turbo Basic program that creates the Eureka equation file for this problem.

The following Turbo Basic program will create a file called PROBLEM and write the data from the arrays into the file in a format suitable for Eureka to solve.

```
OPEN "O", 1, "PROBLEM"
PRINT #1, "$ substlevel = 0"
PRINT #1, "f(x) := exp(A * (x^N) + B)"
FOR I= 1 TO 5
PRINT #1, using "\\#\ \###.##"; "f("; X(I);"):="; Y(I)
NEXT I
CLOSE #1
END
```

Equation File and Solution

The equation file, the solution, and a list of calculated values for this problem appear in the print-out that follows.

```
********************************************************************
Eureka: The Solver, Version 1.0
Sunday November 9, 1986, 3:33 pm.
Name of input file: LSQRFIT.EKA
********************************************************************

; This example demonstrates Eureka's ability to find
; values for constants in a function that make the
; function best fit empirical data. Because the equation
; file includes a $ substlevel = 0 directive, Eureka will
; perform a Least Squares Fit to find the function (of
; the required form) that best matches the points
; (x, f(x)) given.

; In this example, the function is
;     f(x) := EXP(A * x^N + B)
; where the ideal solution is A = 0.25, B = 0.15 and
; N = 1.5

   f(x) := EXP(A * x^N + B)

   f(1) = 1.49
   f(2) = 2.35
   f(3) = 4.26
   f(4) = 8.59
   f(5) = 19.01

$ substlevel = 0

********************************************************************

Solution:

Variables    Values

A        =      .25247836

B        =      .14432763

N        =     1.4951057

Maximum error is -.00011769096

********************************************************************

List of function values.

     x              f(x)

 .00000000      1.1552625
1.0000000       1.4870674
2.0000000       2.3537876
3.0000000       4.2597419
4.0000000       8.5891228
5.0000000      19.010163
6.0000000      45.722423
7.0000000     118.62542
8.0000000     330.10583
9.0000000     980.76072
10.000000    3099.2752

********************************************************************
```

Problem 7
Motion of a Projectile in a Gravitational Field
with Air Resistance

This is a problem in elementary dynamics (PROJCTL.EKA on the distribution disk). You are to find the motion of a projectile in the atmosphere; air resistance and gravity eventually bring the projectile to earth. This problem demonstrates Eureka's ability to solve transcendental functions as well as automatically convert units of measurement.

Statement of the Problem

Consider a projectile that is fired into the air at an angle A with an initial velocity *Vinit*.

If you neglect air resistance, it is easy to show that the path of the projectile is a parabola. With air resistance, the path is a more complicated function (which you derive below). Eventually, the projectile will hit the ground after it has travelled a distance R (the range). In this problem, you find the range (R) and the total flight time (T).

Equations

You will consider the x and y coordinates separately. The initial conditions are:

$x(t) = 0$ when $t = 0$
$y(t) = 0$ when $t = 0$
$x'(0) = Vinit(0)\cos(A) = U$
$y'(0) = Vinit(0)\sin(A) = V$

where x' and y' are the first time derivatives (that is, the velocity).

The equations of motion are:

$mx'' = -kmx'$
$my'' = -kmy' - mg$ (the y-deceleration)

The first of these equations states that the x-deceleration is proportional to the velocity; this is due to air resistance.

The second equation states that the y-deceleration (remember, the projectile is fired upwards) has two terms—an air resistance term and a gravitational term.

The constant k, the drag coefficient, measures the strength of the resistance; g is the acceleration of gravity; and m is the mass of the projectile.

These differential equations can each be solved by integrating twice; the results are:

$$x(t) = (U/k) \times (1 - e^{-kt})$$
$$y(t) = gt/k + ((kV + g)/k^2) \times (1 - e^{-kt})$$

where U and V are the horizontal and vertical components, respectively, of the projectile's initial velocity, $Vinit$.

The total flight time, T, can be calculated from the equation for $y(t)$ by noting that $y = 0$ at the end of the flight; therefore, $y(t = T) = 0$. Solving for T, you get

$$y(T) = 0 = (gT/k) + (((kV + g)/k^2) \times (1 - e^{-kT}))$$
$$T = -((kV + g)/gk) \times (1 - e^{-kT})$$

The range, R, is the distance travelled in the x direction at $t = T$, so

$$R = (U/k) \times (1 - e^{-kT})$$

For typical ballistics problems involving artillery:

- drag coefficient $= 0.1 \times (1/\text{sec})$
- $1{,}000$ ft/s $< Vinit < 3{,}000$ ft/s ($30{,}000$ cm/sec $< Vinit < 90{,}000$ cm/sec)
- acceleration of gravity $= 980$ cm/(sec^2)

Let $Vinit = 50{,}000$ cm/sec, and let $A = 45$ degrees, then

$U = V = 35{,}355$ cm/sec
$T = ((0.1 \times 35{,}355) + 980)/(980 \times 0.1) \times (1 - e^{-.1 \times T})$ sec
$R = (35{,}355/0.1) \times (1 - e^{-0.1 \times T})$ cm

You will use Eureka to solve for T and R.

Equation File and Solution

The print-out that follows shows the equation file and solution for this problem. To simplify the equation for T, we show the calculation of an intermediate constant

```
c = (k * V + g)/(g * k)
```

as a separate line. We also use Eureka's unit conversion directive, so the solution will be displayed in several convenient units.

You can experiment with this problem and see how varying the initial parameters alters the solution. In particular, notice that a significant change to the drag coefficient changes the range of the projectile significantly, while flight time changes slowly.

For example, changing k from 0.1 to 0.001 increases the range by more than 7 times (to 15 miles), but only increases the flight time to 71 seconds.

```
********************************************************************
Eureka: The Solver, Version 1.0
Saturday November 8, 1986, 2:22 pm.
Name of input file: PROJCTL.EKA
********************************************************************


; This example demonstrates solving a typical ballistics
; problem, and Eureka's unit-conversion capability.

  c = ((k*V + g)/(g*k))   ; intermediate constant to
                          ; simplify equation for T
  k = 0.1                 ; drag coefficient
  V = 35355
  V := 35355 [cm/sec]     ; define units of initial velocity
  g = 980                 ; force of gravity

  T = c*(1 - exp(-k*T))   ; solve for total flight time
  T := 40  [sec]
  R = (V/k)*(1 - exp(-k*T))  ; solve for projectile's range
  R := 1  [cm]

 $ units
   cm -> feet : x / (2.54*12)
   cm/sec -> feet/sec : x / (2.54*12)
   feet -> miles : x / 5280
   feet/sec -> miles/hour : x / (5280/3600)
 $ end

********************************************************************

Solution:

Variables   Values

c           =     46.076531

g           =     980.00000

k           =     .10000000

R           =     349848.99 cm
            =     11477.985 feet
            =     2.1738608 miles

T           =     45.594195 sec

V           =     35355.000 cm/sec
            =     1159.9409 feet/sec
            =     790.86883 miles/hour


Maximum error is 7.1054274e-15

********************************************************************
```

Problem 8
Charged Masses in a Gravitational Field

This is a typical problem in electrostatics (MASSCHG.EKA on the distribution disk), illustrating Eureka's ability to find the minimum of a function.

Statement of the Problem

Four negatively charged mass points (for example, pith balls) are constrained to a vertical line (for example, by a non-conducting wire) in a gravitational field. The lowest ball rests on the ground. The problem is to find the equilibrium positions of the other three balls.

As shown in Figure 6-2, the balls lie along the y axis and gravity acts in the negative y direction. The charges repel each other, but the balls are also pulled together by gravity.

The problem is to find the positions where the gravitational pull and electrostatic repulsion balance.

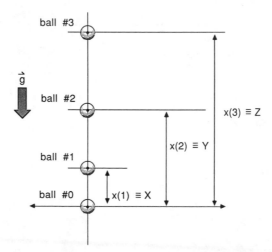

Figure 6-2   *Charged Balls*

You will solve this problem by minimizing the total potential energy of the system. The total potential energy of the system is the sum of the gravitational and electrostatic potential energies of each ball.

The gravitational potential energy of a ball is equal to its mass multiplied by its distance from the ground multiplied by the acceleration of gravity. This value is zero at the ground and increases with increasing height.

The electrostatic potential energy of a ball due to the charge of another is just the charge of the first ball multiplied by the electrostatic potential produced by the other one.

The total potential energy of a ball is the sum of the potential energies due to each of the other balls in the system. This value is defined to be zero for the ball on the ground and positive for all other balls.

Thus, if the four balls are numbered 0 to 3, with number 0 being the ball on the ground, and if

- the masses are m_0 to m_3
- the charges are e_0 to e_3
- the distances from the origin are x_0 to x_3 (with x_0 being zero),

then the following equations express the electrostatic potential energies E_i of each ball:

$$E_0 = 0$$
$$E_1 = e_1[e_0/x_1 + e_2/(x_2 - x_1) + e_3/(x_3 - x_1)]$$
$$E_2 = e_2[e_0/x_2 + e_1/(x_2 - x_1) + e_3/(x_3 - x_2)]$$
$$E_3 = e_3[e_0/x_3 + e_1/(x_3 - x_1) + e_2/(x_3 - x_2)]$$

The individual gravitational potential energies, $G(i)$, have the following form:

$$G_i = m_i g x_i$$

where g is the acceleration of gravity (980 cm/sec^2). The total potential energy of the system, T, is just the sum of all the E_i and G_i:

$$T = \sum_{i=0}^{3} E_i + G_i$$

In order to find the solution, you will use Eureka to find the values for $x(i)$ that minimize T.

Assume that the balls all have a mass of 1 gm and a charge of 80 esu. To avoid the use of subscripts, we will use x, y, and z for the distances x_i. After combining common terms, the expression for T is:

$$T = 980 \times (x + y + z) + 6400 \times [1/x + 1/y + 1/z + 2/(y - x) + 2/(z - x) + 2/(z - y)]$$

Since we are using the CGS system, T is measured in ergs, and x, y, and z are in centimeters.

Equation File and Solution

The print-out that follows shows the equation file used to minimize T. Notice that you must supply the additional constraints $z > y > x > 0$ and $T > 0$, and initial values for x, y, and z. Without these constraints and initial values, Eureka can get lost.

```
****************************************************************
Eureka: The Solver, Version 1.0
Sunday December 7, 1986, 6:23 pm.
Name of input file: MASSCHG.EKA
****************************************************************

$ min (T)

T = 980*(x + y + z) + 6400*(1/x + 1/y + 1/z + 2/(y-x) +
    2/(z-x) + 2/(z-y))

T > 0
T := 29000
x > 0
x := 2 [cm]
y > x
y := 5 [cm]
z > y
z := 10 [cm]
y-x > 0
z-x > 0
z-y >0


****************************************************************

Solution:

Variables      Values

T         =        29900.376

x         =        1.5793519 cm

y         =        4.6531267 cm

z         =        9.0228156 cm

Confidence level =    96.6%
All constraints satisfied.

****************************************************************
```

Problem 9
Using the Built-in Polynomial Function to Find Real and Complex Roots

This problem (POLYNOM.EKA on the distribution disk) demonstrates how to use Eureka's built-in *poly* function to find the roots of *n*th degree polynomials in one variable and illustrates methods for plotting polynomial functions. The *poly* function can find real and complex roots, and, with the Graph/Plot option, can plot the function over a specified, definite range.

Statement of the Problem

Consider the following functions of x:

$$R(x) = x^4 - 2x^3 - 13x^2 + 14x + 24$$
$$S(x) = x^2 - 2x + 5$$
$$T(x) = 2x^2 + 3x + 9$$
$$U(x) = 2x^4 - x^3 + 13x^2 - 3x + 45$$
$$V(x) = 2x^3 - 5x^2 - 3x - 36$$
$$W(x) = 3x^5 + 5x^3 - 7x + 24$$
$$P(x) = x^5 + 1$$

The problem is to find all roots of these polynomials. One of these functions has all real roots, two have all complex roots, and four have a combination of real and complex roots. When you use *poly*, it is not necessary to change the Complex setting to *yes* in order to find the complex roots; Eureka can solve all these problems with a single Solve command.

Equations

To use the *poly* function in Eureka, you only need to enter one equation for each polynomial function to be solved; these are user-defined functions designated by the symbol := .

Each user-defined function states, in terms that Eureka understands, that "some function of x is defined as the polynomial in x that has the following listed coefficients."

When setting up a *poly* function, remember to:

- first list the variable (typically x, but can be any valid variable)
- then list all coefficients of x; start with the highest degree of x, then the next highest, and so on to the constant.

If a polynomial has no coefficient for a given degree of x, then you must enter 0 into the *poly* function for that degree's position, so that Eureka can keep track of each degree of the variable.

For example, using the functions of x given above, the user-defined functions would be written as:

$R(x) := \text{poly}(x, 1, -2, -13, 14, 24)$

$S(x) := \text{poly}(x, 1, -2, 5)$

$T(x) := \text{poly}(x, 2, 3, 9)$

$U(x) := \text{poly}(x, 2, -1, 13, -3, 45)$

$V(x) := \text{poly}(x, 2, -5, -3, -36)$

$W(x) := \text{poly}(x, 3, 0, 5, 0, -7, 24)$

$P(x) := \text{poly}(x, 1, 0, 0, 0, 1)$

Graphing the Functions

Eureka also offers the ability to plot functions of one variable. To graph one of the functions in this problem:

- Solve the equation file.
- Select the Graph option from the main menu.
- From the Graph pull-down menu, choose Plot.
- Select one function from the mini-menu listing of all user-defined functions.
- Enter values for the left and right x axis endpoints.

Eureka will automatically plot the function.

Equation File and Solutions

The print-out that follows shows the equation file and Eureka's solutions for the seven polynomials in this problem.

```
********************************************************************
Eureka: The Solver, Version 1.0
Saturday November 8, 1986, 8:44 pm.
Name of input file: POLYNOM.EKA
********************************************************************


; This problem demonstrates Eureka's built-in Poly
; function, which finds the roots of n-th order
; polynomials of one variable.

; For polynomials in one variable with complex roots,
; you do not need to change the Complex setting to
; yes - Eureka can automatically find complex roots
; when using the Poly function.

; all real roots
; R(x) = (1*x^4 - 2*x^3 - 13*x^2 + 14*x + 24)
R(x) := poly(x,1,-2,-13,14,24)

; all complex roots - Eureka solves for the real part
; of the root being < or = 1
S(x) := poly(x,1,-2,5)

T(x) := poly(x,2,3,9)

; complex and real roots
U(x) := poly(x,2,-1,13,-3,45)

V(x) := poly(x,2,-5,-3,-36)

; some coefficients are zero - they still must be entered
; into the list for Poly
W(x) := poly(x,3,0,5,0,-7,24)

P(x) := poly(x,1,0,0,0,0,1)



********************************************************************
```

```
*******************************************************************

Roots to the polynomial R
#       Real part       Imaginary part
1       -1.0000000      .00000000
2       -3.0000000      .00000000
3        2.0000000      .00000000
4        4.0000000      .00000000

Roots to the polynomial S
#       Real part       Imaginary part
1        1.0000000       2.0000000
2        1.0000000      -2.0000000

Roots to the polynomial T
#       Real part       Imaginary part
1       -.75000000       1.9843135
2       -.75000000      -1.9843135

Roots to the polynomial U
#       Real part       Imaginary part
1        1.0000000       2.0000000
2        1.0000000      -2.0000000
3       -.74999999       1.9843135
4       -.74999999      -1.9843135
Warning: Some roots inaccurate.

Roots to the polynomial V
#       Real part       Imaginary part
1        4.0000000      .00000000
2       -.75000000       1.9843135
3       -.75000000      -1.9843135

Roots to the polynomial W
#       Real part       Imaginary part
3       -1.4464361      .00000000
2       -.28746570       1.7610191
1       -.28746570      -1.7610191
4        1.0106838       .84598193
5        1.0106838      -.84598193

Roots to the polynomial P
#       Real part       Imaginary part
1       -1.0000000      .00000000
2       -.30901699       .95105652
3       -.30901699      -.95105652
4        .80901699       .58778525
5        .80901699      -.58778525


*******************************************************************
```

Problem 10
Maximization: Designing a Maximum-Square-Footage House Plan While Satisfying Several Constraints

This problem (HOUSE.EKA on the distribution disk) shows how to use Eureka to maximize a variable that is a nonlinear function of several other variables, while satisfying constraints placed on the function and on the variables.

Statement of the Problem

In this problem, you are to design an L-shaped house with as much square footage (floor area) as possible, within the limitations imposed by city codes and certain aesthetic considerations. A rectangular second story will be built above the largest part of the first floor, extending from the back wall but only overlapping half of the front wing.

Limitations and Constraints

1. The foundation must encompass no more than 3000 square feet.

2. The width of the front wing (dimensions xy, where x is width) must be within one-third to one-half of the total house width. The total house width is b, and the dimensions of the back wing are ab.

3. The front and back wings will not be disproportionately sized.

4. The house will sit on a 90 x 150-foot lot with 10 foot minimum setbacks on either side and 25 foot minimum setbacks front and back.

5. Leave at least 1,500 square feet in the inside corner of the L for a pool and patio.

Equations

These equations state (1) the purpose of the problem (to maximize the total floor area of the house you design) and (2) the limitations and constraints.

Areas

Area of first floor (covered by foundation):

$B = (xy + ab)$ sq ft

Maximum foundation area allowed by city code:

$B < 3{,}000$ sq ft

Area of second floor (located above front wing of first floor, leaving room for a balcony at front of house):

$A2 = xz$ sq ft

Total area of house (sum of areas of first and second floors):

$A = (xy + ab + xz) = B + xz$ sq ft

Aesthetic constraints

Front wing width is to be between one-third and one-half of total house width b:

$x > b/3$
$x < b/2$

The patio/pool area will occupy the area bordered by the inner walls of the two wings. The dimensions of this area are $(b - x)$ feet by (y) feet, and the total patio/pool area must be at least 1,500 sq ft:

$y \times (b - x) > 1{,}500$

The house width (b) must be less than the lot width (90 ft) minus the two 10-foot setbacks, but it must be at least 40 feet wide:

$b < 68$
$b > 40$

The total house length $(y + a)$ must be less than the lot length (150 ft) minus the two 25-foot setbacks, but it must be at least 56 ft long:

$y + a < 100$
$y + a > 56$

The second story, length (z), must leave half of the extending part of the front wing uncovered:

$z = a + y/2$

The smaller, back-wing extension must extend out at least half as far as the front-wing extension (so the wings will not be disproportionate):

$a > y/2$

The print-out that follows shows the equation file and solution for this maximization problem, along with an evaluation of all the solutions found.

Note the directive $ max (A); that is, the command for Eureka to find the maximum combined first- and second-floor area possible within the listed constraints.

Also note that the equation file includes initial values for b and y. Since this problem contains many conditions that the few variables must satisfy, it is a good idea to get Eureka started in the right direction with some good first guesses.

If you run this problem on your computer, you may notice that it seems to take a relatively long time to reach the solutions. This is normal for a problem like this, which contains many constraints for just a few variables. Watch the Progress window for information about how Eureka is handling the problem.

```
********************************************************************
Eureka: The Solver, Version 1.0
Saturday November 8, 1986, 9:02 pm.
Name of input file: HOUSE.EKA
********************************************************************


; This problem illustrates maximizing a nonlinear
; function while satisfying several constraints on the
; function and on the variables.  Notice that we maximize
; a variable, A, which is related to the other variables
; x, y, z, a and b according to the first equation.

$ max (A)

; maximize area within limits of city code
A = (x*y + a*b + x*z) = B + x*z
B = (x*y + a*b)
B < 3000

; aesthetic constraints
x > b/3
x < b/2

; leave room for patio/pool
y*(b-x) > 1500

; set-backs and more aesthetics
b < 68  :  b > 40
y+a < 100  :  y+a > 56
z = a + y/2
a > y/2

; initial values
b:=68
y:=56


********************************************************************
```

```
********************************************************************

Solution:

Variables    Values

A         =    4500.0000

a         =    23.677311

B         =    3000.0000

b         =    63.351788

x         =    31.675894

y         =    47.354622

z         =    47.354622


Confidence level =   92.3%
All constraints satisfied.

Evaluation of formulas:

Formulas        Values

A           =     4500.0000
(x*y+a*b+x*z)  =     4500.0000
    difference =     .00000000

B+x*z       =     4500.0000
    difference =     .00000000


B           =     3000.0000
(x*y+a*b)   =     3000.0000
    difference =     .00000000

B           =     3000.0000
3000        =     3000.0000
    difference = -4.9408300e-08
********************************************************************
```

```
********************************************************************

x                  =        31.675894
b/3                =        21.117263
     difference =        10.558631

x                  =        31.675894
b/2                =        31.675894
     difference = -2.9878677e-10

y*(b-x)            =        1500.0000
1500               =        1500.0000
     difference (error) = -4.0927262e-12

b                  =        63.351788
68                 =        68.000000
     difference =        -4.6482119
b                  =        63.351788
40                 =        40.000000
     difference =        23.351788

y+a                =        70.031933
100                =        100.00000
     difference =        -28.968067

y+a                =        70.031933
56                 =        56.000000
     difference =        15.031933

z                  =        47.354622
a+y/2              =        47.354622
     difference =        .00000000

a                  =        23.677311
y/2                =        23.677311
     difference (error) = -1.0976464e-10

b                  =        63.351788
y                  =        47.354622

Maximum error is -1.0976464e-10

********************************************************************
```

Problem 11
Maximization: Linear Programming in Manufacturing

This example, a problem in linear programming (LINPROG.EKA on the distribution disk) demonstrates Eureka's ability to solve simultaneous linear equations in multiple variables and to maximize the objective function in order to reach an optimum solution.

Statement of the Problem

Suppose a company makes two types of widgets, one wooden and one plastic. To make a wooden widget, the producer uses machine A for 2 hours, machine B for 1 hour and machine C for 1 hour. To make a plastic widget requires 1 hour of machining on A, 2 hours on B, and 1 hour on C. The maximum amount of time (per month) available on machine A is 180 hours; on B, 160 hours; and on C, 100 hours. The profit on each wooden widget is $4.00 and on each plastic one $6.00.

Assuming that all widgets made will sell, how many of each type should the company make in order to maximize the monthly profit?

Equations

Hours	Machine A	Machine B	Machine C	Profit (per unit)
To make wooden widgets	2	1	1	$4.00
To make plastic widgets	1	2	1	$6.00
Available per month	180	160	100	—

Profit Function (the Objective Function)

First, assign variables to each model of widget, with x being the monthly manufactured amount of the wooden variety and y being the same for the plastic widgets. Monthly profit is then the sum of the individual profits:

Profit $= 4x + 6y$

This is the objective function that you are going to maximize. To maximize the objective function, use Eureka's built-in maximization function. Add the *max* directive to the file:

```
$ max (Profit)
```

Remember that the *max* directive can be used only once per equation file.

To avoid a solution which says that only the higher-profit plastic model will be manufactured, set

```
x > 0 ; wooden widgets
y > 0 ; plastic widgets
```

Since the total time on machine A can't exceed 180 hours per month and the manufacturing processes require 2 hours of machine A's time for a wooden widget or 1 hour for a plastic widget, write the following constraint to represent the time limitation:

```
2 * x + y < 180
```

Similarly, write constraints for the manufacturing time on machines B and C:

```
x + 2 * y < 160 ; total time on machine B can't exceed 160 hours per month
x + y < 100     ; total time on machine C can't exceed 100 hours per month
```

Equation File and Solution

The print-out that follows shows the equation file and solution for this problem.

Notice that we have started Eureka off with some initial values for x and y. We chose initial values that represented the maximum possible value for each variable that would satisfy the manufacturing-time constraints. Although this is not necessary, it may help to speed up Eureka's search for a solution; the default value for both x and y at the beginning of the search is 1.0.

Notice also that we did *not* set the *Profit* function up as a user-defined function; we used the equal sign (=) for an assignment operator, not the colon-equals operator (:=). This is an important distinction; if you were to write the objective function as Profit := (4 * x + 6 * y), Eureka would interpret that as meaning that *Profit* is a variable to be maximized (due to the *max* directive) and it merely has a starting point value of 4 * x + 6 * y. The result would be that Eureka maximizes *Profit* to the rather high value of 1.1529215 * 10^20 (dollars).

```
**********************************************************************
Eureka: The Solver, Version 1.0
Saturday November 8, 1986, 9:06 pm.
Name of input file: LINPROG.EKA
**********************************************************************


; This example, a problem in linear programming, demon-
; strates Eureka's ability to solve simultaneous linear
; equations in multiple variables, and to maximize the
; objective function in order to reach an optimum
; solution.

; Equations

; Profit function (the objective function)

   Profit = (4*x) + (6*y)
   $ max (Profit)

   x > 0  ; wooden widgets
   y > 0  ; plastic widgets

   x := 90
   y := 80

   2*x + y < 180  ; total time on machine A can't exceed 180
   x + 2*y < 160  ; total time on machine B can't exceed 160
   x + y < 100  ; total time on machine C can't exceed 100

**********************************************************************

Solution:

Variables    Values

Profit    =    520.00000

x         =    40.000000

y         =    60.000000


Confidence level =   93.1%
All constraints satisfied.


**********************************************************************
```

Problem 12
Equity in a House: the paymt, pval and fval functions

This example (EQUITY.EKA on the distribution disk) is a simple problem in finance. Using some of Eureka's built-in functions, you will calculate the growth in the equity in a house purchased with a mortgage.

Statement of the Problem

Suppose you purchase a house on January 1 for $200,000, using a $20,000 down payment and a 13% 30-year fixed-rate mortgage for $180,000. Assume that the mortgage interest compounds monthly and that your payments are made monthly. Use Eureka to calculate:

1. Your monthly payments.

2. How long it will take for your equity in the house to increase to $100,000.

Equations

Eureka has several built-in functions that are useful in financial calculations. These functions compute the key values in interest-rate calculations. In this example, you will use the *paymt* and *fval* functions.

paymt calculates the payment in each interval on the loan, using as inputs the interest rate, the number of intervals, and the present and final value of the loan.

fval calculates the future value of a loan, using as inputs the present value, the payment per interval, the number of intervals until the future date, and the interest rate.

These are the input parameters:

number of payment intervals	N	$= 30 \times 12 = 360$ months
interest rate per interval	I	$= .13/12$
price of house	P	$= 200,000$
down payment	D	$= 20,000$
value of mortgage (principal)	pval	$= 180,000$
amount of balloon payment due	B	$= 0$

You need to calculate the size of the monthly payments (*mp*) and the number of months (*time*) until the equity is $100,000. The monthly payment can be found by simply plugging the input parameters into *paymt* in the following order:

mp = paymt(*I*, *N*, *P-D*, *B*) which leads to

mp = paymt(0.13/12, 30 * 12, 180000, 0)

where the final 0 is the final value of the mortgage after 30 years (in this example, there is no balloon payment).

Equity in the house is simply the difference between what the house is worth and what you still owe the bank. The equity will be $100,000 at some future time that can be calculated using the *fval* function:

Future Value of Mortgage = fval(*I*, *time*, *L*, *mp*)

which gives

100,000 = 200,000 + fval(.13/12, *time*, 180000, *mp*)

You can now solve these two equations for *mp* and *time* to determine the regular monthly payment and the elapsed time (in months) until the equity reaches $100,000.00.

Equation File and Solution

The Eureka equation file corresponding to these equations is shown in the print-out that follows.

Notice that the first entry in the equation file is a directive (set off with the $ symbol) to set *finansmooth* to *on*. This is necessary because financial functions are typically discontinuous in time. With *finansmooth on*, Eureka automatically smooths out the discontinuities and converts the financial function to a smooth curve instead of a series of step functions.

```
******************************************************************
Eureka: The Solver, Version 1.0
Tuesday February 10, 1987, 5:33 pm.
Name of input file: EQUITY.EKA
******************************************************************


; This problem shows how to use Eureka's
; built-in financial function PAYMT to
; calculate monthly payments for a 30-year,
; $180,000.00 mortgage, with a $20,000.00
; down payment and a yearly interest rate
; of 13%.

; This problem also demonstrates using
; the built-in function FVAL to calculate
; when the equity reaches $100,000.00, and
; calculates the balance of the loan at
; any given time.
; Note: this problem incorporates zero
; market appreciation.

$ finansmooth = yes

; variables assigned to the given data:
    DownPay = 20000
    Loan = 180000
    Duration = 30 * 12

; determining monthly interest rate from
; the annual rate
    Yrate = 0.13
    Mrate = Yrate / 12

; finding the monthly payment
    Payment = PAYMT(Mrate,Duration,
                    Loan,0)

; formula for determining Equity at a
; given time:
    FutureValue(GivenMonth):=FVAL(Mrate,_
         GivenMonth,Loan,Payment)
    Equity(GivenMonth) := DownPay + Loan + FVAL(Mrate,_
         GivenMonth,Loan,Payment)
    Equity(HowSoon) = 100000

; formula for determining total amount
; paid at the end of the life of the
; loan
    TotalPaid = Payment * Duration

; Amount still owed on loan at any given
; month
    AmtOwed(GivenMonth) := Loan + DownPay - Equity(GivenMonth)
```

Solution:

Variables		Values
DownPay	=	20000.000
Duration	=	360.00000
HowSoon	=	287.10773
Loan	=	180000.00
Mrate	=	.010833333
Payment	=	-1991.1591
TotalPaid	=	-716817.29
Yrate	=	.13000000

Maximum error is .011900878

List of function values.
Equity

x	Equity(x)
12.000000	20524.427
24.000000	21121.243
36.000000	21800.438
48.000000	22573.385
60.000000	23453.023
72.000000	24454.080
84.000000	25593.315
96.000000	26889.801
108.00000	28365.245
120.00000	30044.348
132.00000	31955.222
144.00000	34129.859
156.00000	36604.665
168.00000	39421.076
180.00000	42626.243
192.00000	46273.827
204.00000	50424.896
216.00000	55148.947
228.00000	60525.071
240.00000	66643.275
252.00000	73605.989
264.00000	81529.784
276.00000	90547.320
288.00000	100809.57
300.00000	112488.34
312.00000	125779.17
324.00000	140904.55
336.00000	158117.74
348.00000	177706.90
360.00000	200000.00

****

Problem 13
Probability in a Card Game

This problem (CARDS.EKA on the distribution disk) illustrates Eureka's built-in factorial function, *fact,* and demonstrates how to set up a user-defined function.

Statement of the Problem

In a game of Bridge, find the probability that a trump suit with six trumps outstanding will split three-three.

For those who do not play Bridge, here is a synopsis of how to play the game:

There are 13 cards dealt to each of 4 players. Of these, 13 of the cards are trumps. When a player says s/he is hoping for a three-three trump split, it is because s/he controls 2 of the hands and 7 of the trumps, with the remaining 6 trumps divided between the remaining 2 hands in an unknown manner. The trumps are said to split three-three if there are exactly 3 trumps in each of the unknown hands.

Equations

Stating the problem in different terms, we can ask how many combinations of N *choose* M exist for this problem, where N *choose* M represents the number of unique ways to choose a subset of size M from a set of N items.

In standard mathematical notation, this is expressed as a "combinatorial coefficient" (*CofNandM*) where

$$CofNandM = \frac{(N!)}{(M!) \times ((N-M)!)}$$

If you (perhaps naively) assume that the probability of distributing six things randomly yields a three-three split, the equation for the (approximate) probability is:

$ProbApprox = C(6,3) / 2^6$

If you assume that the probability of random distribution does not yield a three-three split, the exact probability for an even split is:

$$ProbExact = \frac{C(26,13)}{C(20,10)} \times C(6,3)$$

Equation File and Solution

The print-out that follows shows the equation file and solution for this problem.

```
********************************************************************
Eureka: The Solver, Version 1.0
Saturday November 8, 1986, 10:46 pm.
Name of input file: CARDS.EKA
********************************************************************
```

; This example demonstrates how to use Eureka's built-in
; FACT function (FACT(x) = x factorial). The problem
; is:
; In a Bridge game, one player controls 7 trump cards.
; We must determine the probability that the remaining
; 6 trump cards are evenly distributed (3 and 3) among
; the other two players. We calculate both the
; approximate and the exact probability in this example.

A(x) := FACT(x)
C6 = A(6)
C3 = A(3)
C10 = A(10)
C20 = A(20)
C26 = A(26)
C13 = A(13)

; The combinatorial coefficients for total available
; cards and cards per remaining hand:

Cof6and3 = A(6) / (A(3) * A(6-3))
Cof20and10 - A(20) / (A(10) * A(20-10))
Cof26and13 = A(26) / (A(13) * A(26-13))

; approximate probability of 3-3 split:
ProbApprox = Cof6and3 / 2^6

; exact probability of 3-3 split:
   ProbExact = Cof6and3 * Cof20and10 / Cof26and13

; The correct answers are
;   ProbApprox = .3125
;   ProbExact = .355279503

Solution:

Variables   Values

C10   =   3628800.0

C13   = 6.2270208e+09

C20   = 2.4329020e+18

C26   = 4.0329146e+26

C3   =   6.0000000

C6   =   720.00000

Cof20and10   =   184756.00

Cof26and13   =   10400600.

Cof6and3   =   20.000000

ProbApprox   =   .31250000

ProbExact   =   .35527950

****

Problem 14
Income Distribution: The integ Function

This problem (INTEG.EKA on the distribution disk) demonstrates how to use Eureka's built-in *integ* function to calculate the definite integral of functions.

Statement of the Problem

In the study of income distributions, one useful quantitative measure is the Lorentz Curve, a function relating the cumulative percentage of income recipients (x) to the cumulative percentage of income (y). The equality of income distribution given by the line $x = y$ represents the ideal state, where income is evenly distributed among the whole population: 10% of the people receive 10% of the income, 30% receive 30%, and so on.

A more realistic, non-ideal income distribution is the function

$$y = (20/21)x^2 + (1/21)x$$

The coefficient of inequality measures the degree of deviation from equality; this coefficient is defined as the area between the income-distribution curve and the diagonal ($x = y$), divided by the area under the diagonal. When all incomes are evenly and equally distributed, the coefficient of inequality becomes zero.

The problem: For the income-distribution function given above, what is the coefficient of inequality?

Equations

To solve this problem, you must integrate two functions from 0 to 1 (0 to 100%), then calculate a quotient using the two integrals. With Eureka's built-in *integ* function, this is an easy exercise. From the definition of the coefficient of inequality given above, define the numerator (*Num*) and denominator (*Denom*) as the integrals of the two functions given:

Num is the difference between the definite integral of the diagonal ($x = y$) and the definite integral of the function ($y(x)$):

Num = [integral(x) − integral(($20/21)x^2 + (1/21)x$)] from $x = 0$ to $x = 1$

Denom is the definite integral of the function:

$y = x$ from $x = 0$ to $x = 1$

The coefficient of inequality is the quotient

```
CoeffInEq = Num/Denom
```

Using the *integ* function, this is how you set up the two integrals:

```
Num = integ(x, x, 0, 1) - integ((20/21)*x^2 + (1/21)*x, x, 0, 1)
Denom = integ(x, x, 0, 1)
```

Equation File and Solution

The print-out that follows shows the equation file and the solution for the problem. The table at the end of the print-out shows the result of selecting Graph/List.

```
********************************************************************
Eureka: The Solver, Version 1.0
Saturday November 8, 1986, 11:40 am.
Name of input file: INTEG.EKA
********************************************************************


; This problem demonstrates how to use Eureka's built-in
; INTEG function to perform definite integrals.  The
; example comes from the study of income distributions.

; income distribution function (Lorentz curve - non-ideal)
   y(x) := (20/21)*x^2 + (1/21)*x

   Num = INTEG(x, x, 0, 1) - INTEG((20/21)*x^2 + (1/21)*x, x, 0, 1)
   Denom = INTEG(x, x, 0, 1)

; coefficient of inequality:
   CoeffInEq = Num/Denom

********************************************************************

Solution:

Variables     Values

CoeffInEq  =     0.31746032

Denom      =     0.5000000

Num        =     0.15873016

List of function values.

      x           y(x)
 .00000000      .00000000
 .10000000      .014285714
 .20000000      .047619048
 .30000000      .10000000
 .40000000      .17142857
 .50000000      .26190476
 .60000000      .37142857
 .70000000      .50000000
 .80000000      .64761905
 .90000000      .81428571
1.0000000      1.0000000


********************************************************************
```

Problem 15
Chemical Calculations

This problem (CHEMBAL.EKA, CHEMEQ1.EKA, CHEMEQ2.EKA, and CHEMEQ3.EKA on the distribution disk) illustrates how you can use Eureka to solve problems in chemistry, from the simple-but-tedious (balancing chemical equations) to the more sophisticated (calculating equilibrium concentrations).

The first part of this problem:

- demonstrates Eureka's ability to solve some simple systems of linear equations

- identifies a situation where the *include* directive would be useful

- gives a quick method for balancing chemical equations and determining unknown stoichiometric quantities

The second part of the problem gives three examples of calculating equilibrium concentrations, including a classic difficult problem where poorly-scaled variables hamper Eureka's solution process.

Part I: The Reaction of Iron Sulfide with Oxygen to Produce Iron Oxide and Sulfur Dioxide

This problem in stoichiometry (CHEMBAL.EKA on the distribution disk) asks you to find out how much of a reactant is needed for a chemical reaction to produce a certain amount of product.

Statement of the Problem

Consider the chemical reaction between FeS and O_2, written here as an unbalanced chemical equation:

$$FeS + O_2 \rightarrow Fe_2O_3 + SO_2$$

How much iron sulfide (in grams) is required to produce 100 grams of iron oxide in this reaction?

To solve this problem, you will first need to balance the chemical equation. In addition, you will need to convert the given mass information (in this case, 100 grams of Fe_2O_3) into its molar equivalent.

A *mole* is defined as the formula weight (in grams) of an element or compound. It is also, by definition, the mass of a specified number of molecules of a substance. The specified number is Avogadro's number (6.0221×10^{23} molecules.)

Once you know the ratios between the different substances in the reaction and the given number of moles (of product, in this case), you can determine the number of moles of other substances that satisfy the given requirement.

Equations

You can assign variables for all the unknown amounts in the unbalanced chemical equation and set up the following algebraic expression to represent the balanced state:

```
a * (Fe + S) + b * (0 * 2) - c * (Fe * 2 + 0 * 3) - d * (S + 0 * 2) = 0
```

Since elements cannot just appear or disappear, the net amounts of each element must be the same on each side of the balanced equation. This means that the variables for each of the elements have the following relationships:

for Fe, $a = 2c$
for S, $a = d$
for O, $2b = 3c + 2d$

The solutions to these variables will yield a balanced chemical equation, which specifies the number of moles of reactants used in the chemical reaction and the number of moles of products that result.

The next step is to write an equation for converting the given information (100 grams of Fe_2O_3) into moles.

Remember that chemical symbols (Fe, K, Ca, Na, O, S, and so on) are just that — symbols — and can be manipulated just like variables in equations. You can combine these symbols with each other and with constants representing mass, valence, atomic number, or any other property that you need to factor in when solving chemical equations.

For example, consider Fe_2O_3 and the following definitions:

mFe $\quad$ = mass of one mole of Fe (55.847 grams)
zFe $\quad$ = atomic number of Fe (26)
vFe $\quad$ = valence of Fe (2 or 3; depends on particular compound)
mO $\quad$ = mass of one mole of O (15.9994 grams)
zO $\quad$ = atomic number of O (8)
vO $\quad$ = valence of O (typically, -2)
mFe$_2$O$_3$ = mass of one mole of Fe_2O_3 = $(m\text{Fe} \times 2) + (m\text{O} \times 3)$

similarly,

mFeS = mFe + mS
mSO$_2$ = mS + $(m\text{O} \times 2)$

To convert measured amounts of substances into their molar equivalents, you divide the measured amount by the mole weight:

$$\frac{100.00 \text{ gm of } Fe_2O_3}{159.69 \text{ gm/mole}} = \frac{100.00}{159.69} = 0.6262 \text{ moles of } Fe_2O_3$$

The amount of each substance used or produced in the chemical reaction can be represented by a "how much?" variable, written by adding h to the beginning of each chemical formula. In this example, "how much Fe_2O_3?" is represented by hFe_2O_3 and is the given quantity — 100 grams. Similarly, $hFeS$ represents "how much FeS?", the amount (in grams) of FeS used, and hO_2 represents the amount of O_2 consumed.

In terms of the variables in this problem, the number of moles of Fe_2O_3 is calculated by

$$\frac{\text{howmuch } Fe_2O_3}{\text{mass of one mole of } Fe_2O_3} = \frac{hFe_2O_3}{mFe_2O_3}$$

where $mFe_2O_3 = 159.69$ and hFe_2O_3 is the given, 100 grams.

You can see that the number of moles of Fe_2O_3 produced is equal to the number of moles of FeS supplied. This can be rephrased as:

a moles of FeS produce c moles of Fe_2O_3

so the ratio of (moles of FeS):(moles of Fe_2O_3) is the ratio $a:c$. The equation for this is

$$\frac{\text{moles of FeS}}{\text{moles of } Fe_2O_3} = \frac{a}{c}$$

which leads to the equation

$$c \times (\text{moles of FeS}) = a \times (\text{moles of } Fe_2O_3)$$

By substituting the number of moles equation from above, you get

$$c \times \frac{hFeS}{mFeS} = a \times \frac{hFe_2O_3}{mFe_2O_3}$$

Eureka will solve for the variables a and c in the first part of this problem; $mFeS$ and mFe_2O_3 are constants and hFe_2O_3 is the given, so you can easily solve for the unknown quantity, $hFeS$.

Equation File and Solution

The print-out that follows shows the Eureka equation file and solution for this problem.

Eureka will solve this system of linear equations and give values for a, b, c, and d that balance the chemical equation.

To get Eureka started, you assign a value to one of the variables and see what solutions the program finds. This is not necessary, but it helps to keep the solutions for a, b, c, and d as whole numbers.

You can see from the equation for the variable b that c should be an even number so b will be an integer; that is why we set c equal to 2.

Besides giving a value to one of the variables, you must include the values for the given amount of product (100 grams of Fe_2O_3) and the constant values. In this case, the constant values are the mole weights of the elements Fe, O, and S.

Using the $ include Directive

You can experiment with this problem, or similar ones, to explore Eureka's usefulness in stoichiometry. If you plan to be solving many problems such as this one, you will probably find it helpful to create a separate file containing the mole weights for all the elements that you will be dealing with. Keeping such a file as a permanent part of your Eureka problem disk, you could use the *include* directive in your equation file to call up the mole weight information when it is needed instead of entering it over and over.

```
********************************************************************
Eureka: The Solver, Version 1.0
Thursday November 6, 1986, 6:11 am.
Name of input file: CHEMBAL.EKA
********************************************************************


; This is an example of balancing a chemical equation
; and then finding the amount of reactant, FeS, needed to
; yield 100.00 grams of Fe2O3 product

; the unbalanced chemical equation:
; FeS + O2 --> Fe2O3 + SO2

; algebraic expression for the balanced equation:
; a*FeS + b*O2 --> c*Fe2O3 + d*SO2

a = 2*c
d = a
b*2 = 3*c + 2*d

c = 2.000

; mole weights (grams/mole)

mFe = 55.847
mS  = 28.086
mO  = 15.9994


mFeS   = mFe + mS
mFe2O3 = mFe*2 + mO*3
mO2    = mO*2
mSO2   = mS + mO*2

; amount of product required is 100 grams
hFe2O3 = 100.00

; ratio of moles of FeS to moles of Fe2O3 is a:c
c*(hFeS/mFeS) = a*(hFe2O3/mFe2O3)

; correct answer is a = d = 4, b = 7, c = 2
```

```
********************************************************************

Solution:

Variables      Values

a          =     4.0000000

b          =     7.0000000

c          =     2.0000000

d          =     4.0000000

hFe2O3     =     100.00000

hFeS       =     105.11847

mFe        =     55.847000

mFe2O3     =     159.69220

mFeS       =     83.933000

mO         =     15.999400

mO2        =     31.998800

mS         =     28.086000

mSO2       =     60.084800

********************************************************************
```

Part II: Calculating Chemical Equilibrium Concentrations

The second part of this problem (CHEMEQ1.EKA, CHEMEQ2.EKA, and CHEMEQ3.EKA on the distribution disk) demonstrates Eureka's ability to solve high-order polynomials by finding equilibrium concentrations for the reactants and products in some sample reversible chemical reactions.

Statement of the Problem

Many chemical reactions do not proceed to completion (that is, all the available reactants are not converted into products) because the reaction is reversible. Some of the products actually react chemically and convert back into their original constituents.

Some examples of such reversible reactions are:

$$H_2(gas) + I_2(gas) \quad \Leftrightarrow 2HI(gas)$$
$$N_2(gas) + 3H_2(gas) \Leftrightarrow 2NH_3(gas)$$

When the rate of forward reaction (in these examples, the combining action of the gases) and the rate of decomposition reach a balance, the chemical reaction is said to be in equilibrium.

At equilibrium at a given temperature, such a reversible chemical reaction can be characterized by an equilibrium constant, K_{eq}. The equilibrium constant is the ratio of two numbers: The first is a product of the concentrations of all the substances on the right-hand side of the chemical equation, and the second is a product of the concentrations of all the substances on the left-hand side. (If a substance in the chemical equation has a coefficient a, then the concentration for that substance is raised to the ath power when calculating K_{eq} for the reversible reaction.)

Laboratory scientists have determined K_{eq}s for many reactions at specific temperatures. If you know the K_{eq} for a reaction and have enough additional information about the reactants or the products, you can determine the equilibrium concentrations of all the substances involved in the reaction.

First Example

Consider the reaction of carbon monoxide (CO) and steam:

$$CO + H_2O \Leftrightarrow CO_2 + H_2$$

At 800°C, the K_{eq} for this reaction is 1.2. If you put 2.0 moles of CO and 2.0 moles of H_2O into a 10-liter container at 800°C, what will be the equilibrium concentrations of all the substances?

Equations

The first step in setting up this problem is to write out a table that lists the starting and equilibrium concentrations for the substances involved.

	Starting Concentration	Equilibrium Concentration
CO	0.2 moles/L	$0.2 - X$ moles/L
H_2O	0.2 moles/L	$0.2 - X$ moles/L
CO_2	0	X moles/L
H_2	0	X moles/L

By definition of the equilibrium constant,

$$K_{eq} = \frac{cCO_2 \times cH_2}{cCO \times cH_2O}$$

Substituting in the values for K_{eq} and the four concentrations from the table yields

$$1.2 = \frac{(X)(X)}{(0.2 - X)(0.2 - X)}$$

$$1.2 = \frac{X^2}{(0.2 - X)^2}$$

You will rewrite these equations as a second-order polynomial and let Eureka solve for X; then, knowing X, Eureka will calculate the equilibrium concentrations of all the reactants and products.

Equation File and Solution

The print-out that follows shows the equation file and the solution for this problem.

Note that we have given an initial value to X in the equation file ($X := 0.19$). We made an assumption that at least 5% of the original substances were converted into products. Although it was not theoretically necessary to provide Eureka with that starting point, it turned out to be a practical action. Without a reasonable initial value for X, Eureka is capable of finding some solutions that are unique but wrong (such as concentrations less than 0). The easiest way to avoid such solutions is to provide Eureka with a reasonable starting point of where you expect the answer to be, if possible.

```
********************************************************************
Eureka: The Solver, Version 1.0
Thursday November 6, 1986, 6:23 am.
Name of input file: CHEMEQ1.EKA
********************************************************************


; Chemical Equilibrium Calculations - First Example
; This problem demonstrates solving a second-order
; polynomial in order to calculate equilibrium
; concentrations in a reversible chemical reaction

; The reaction is:  CO + H2O <===> CO2 + H2

; At 800 degrees C, the Keq for this reaction is 1.2

cCO2 = X          ; equil. conc. of CO2
cH2 = X           ; equil. conc. of H2
cCO = 0.2 - X     ; equil. conc. of CO
cH2O = 0.2 - X    ; equil. conc. of H2O

; Keq = (cCO2 * cH2) / (cCO * cH2O)
1.2 = X^2 / (0.2 - X)^2

; initial value given for X
X:= 0.19

; correct answers are: cCO2 = cH2 = X = .104555
; cCO = cH2O = 0.2 - X = .0954451

********************************************************************

Solution:

Variables    Values

cCO       =    .095445115

cCO2      =    .10455488

cH2       =    .10455488

cH2O      =    .095445115

X         =    .10455488

Maximum error is -1.0924639e-10

********************************************************************
```

Second Example

Consider the reversible reaction of nitrogen (N_2) and hydrogen (H_2) to form ammonia:

$$N_2(gas) + 3H_2(gas) \Leftrightarrow 2NH_3(gas)$$

Empirical evidence shows that log(base 10) of K_f, the equilibrium constant for the forward reaction of N_2 and H_2 to form NH_3, is 2.914 at 25°C.

$$K_f = 10^{2.914}$$

$$\frac{(cNH_3)^2}{cN_2 \times (cH_2)^3} = 10^{2.914}$$

In this problem, you start with .1 mole of N_2 and .3 moles of H_2 in a 10-liter flask at 25°C:

	Starting Concentration	Final Concentration
N_2	0.1 moles/L	$(0.1 - X)$ moles/L
H_2	0.3 moles/L	$(0.3 - 3X)$ moles/L
NH_3	0.0 moles/L	$2X$ moles/L

What will be the concentrations of all the constituents at equilibrium?

Equations

The following polynomial results from substituting the concentration values from the table into the equation for K_f:

$$\frac{(2X)^2}{(0.1 - X)((0.3 - 3X)^3)} = 10^{2.914} = K$$

which simplifies to

$$0 = (K \times 27(0.1 - X)^4) - (2X)^2$$

Equation File and Solution

The equation file and solution for this problem appear in the print-out that follows.

Notice the constraints placed on the value X (which represents the equilibrium concentration of NH_3):

- $X > 0$ (There must be some NH_3 produced)
- $X < 0.1$ (You can't have more products than the reactants)

```
******************************************************************
Eureka: The Solver, Version 1.0
Thursday November 6, 1986, 6:27 am.
Name of input file: CHEMEQ2.EKA
******************************************************************


; Chemical Equilibrium Calculations - Second example
; This is an example of solving a fourth-degree
; polynomial, in order to find the equilibrium
; concentrations of N2, H2 and NH3 in the reversible
; chemical reaction
;        N2 + 3H2 <===> 2NH3
; at 25 degrees C, where log(base 10) of K(f) (the
; equilibrium constant for the forward reaction) is
; 2.914.

K = 10^(2.914)

cN2 = 0.1 - X      ; equil. conc. of N2
cH2 = 0.3 - 3*X    ; equil. conc of H2
cNH3 = 2*X         ; equil. conc. of NH3

; equation for equilibrium concentrations:
; K = (cNH3)^2 / (cN2* (cH2)^3)

4*(X^2) = K * (0.1 - X) * (0.3 - 3*X)^3

; constraints so Eureka finds appropriate roots

0 < X < 0.1

******************************************************************

Solution:

Variables    Values

cH2       =    .091649822

cN2       =    .030549941

cNH3      =    .13890012

K         =    820.35154

X         =    .069450059

Maximum error is -4.2344429e-10

******************************************************************
```

Third Example

This example is a classic case of poorly scaled variables and equations and clearly demonstrates where and how things could go wrong in your equation files.

Consider the dissociation of hydrogen peroxide at 800°C to yield water (H_2O) and oxygen (O_2):

$$2 \times H_2O_2 \Leftrightarrow 2 \times H_2O + O_2$$

At 800°C, the Keq for this reaction is 3.6×10^{13}. If you start with 0.1 mole of H_2O_2 in a 10-liter container at 800°C, what will be the equilibrium concentrations of all the substances?

Equations

	Starting Concentration	Equilibrium Concentration
cH_2O_2	0.01 moles/L	$0.01 - 2X$ moles/L
cO_2	0 moles/L	X moles/L
cH_2O	0 moles/L	$2X$ moles/L

$$K_{eq} = \frac{cO_2(cH_2O)^2}{(cH_2O_2)^2}$$

$$3.6 \times 10^{13} = \frac{(X)(2X)^2}{(0.01 - 2X)^2}$$

$$= \frac{4X^3}{(0.01 - 2X)^2}$$

Since 3.6×10^{13} is a very large number with respect to the other quantities in this problem, the equation is poorly scaled. Eureka runs into difficulty when trying to solve an equation that spans so many orders of magnitude (14 in this case). For example, Eureka might find a solution that yields an evaluation difference of 10^6. Because 10^6 is relatively tiny compared to 10^{13}, Eureka might be satisfied with the solution, even though that solution would be patently wrong.

Given these problems inherent with spanning large orders of magnitude, it would seem that you could convert both sides of the equation to the natural logs and ask Eureka to solve the following:

```
ln (3.6 * 10^13) = ln (4) + ln (X^3) - ln ((0.001 - (2 * X))^2)
```

However, rewriting the original equation to this form does not work well, because Eureka must calculate each of the natural logs used; the problem in this form becomes unworkable.

Your best approach to this quandary is to formulate an intermediate equation that spans fewer orders of magnitude. To accomplish this, create the following set of intermediate variables and equations:

1. substitute Keq = W^3 so W = 36^(1/3) * 10^4

   Y = (0.01 − (2 * X))

   W^3 = 4X^3/Y^2 so W = X * ((2/Y) ^ (2/3))

2. substitute B = (Y/2)^(2/3) so B * W = X

3. set constraints and initializations

   0 < X < 0.005, W > 0, B > 0,

   X := 0.0001

By redefining the problem as B * W = X, you create a situation where the difference between the largest and smallest values is on the order of 10^7 (from 10^4 to 10^{-3}), which Eureka is able to solve in just a few seconds.

Note: It is important to set up the equations in the order shown on the next page. If you present the equations in a different order, Eureka gives an "Equations are inconsistent" error message and cannot solve the problem.

Equation File and Solution

The print-out that follows shows the equation file and Eureka's solution for this problem.

```
********************************************************************
Eureka: The Solver, Version 1.0
Thursday November 6, 1986, 6:32 am.
Name of input file: CHEMEQ3.EKA
********************************************************************

; Chemical Equilibrium Calculation - Third Example

; This example demonstrates how to handle a poorly-scaled
; problem.  The original equation was
;    Keq = 3.6 * 10^13
;    Y = (0.01 - (2*X))
;    4*X^3 / Y^2 = Keq

; To reduce the total span of 14 orders of magnitude,
; substitute W (= Keq^(1/3)) and B (= (Y/2)^(2/3))

W = 36^(1/3) * 10^4
Keq = W^3

B*W = X

B = (Y/2)^(2/3)
Y = (0.01 - (2*X))

X > 0
X < 0.005
W > 0
X := 0.0001
B > 0

; Solution is X = 0.0043698957, Y = 0.0012602085
; B = 1.3234379e-07, W = 33019.272, Keq = 3.6 * 10^13

********************************************************************

Solution:

Variables    Values

B         = 1.3234379e-07

Keq       = 3.6000000e+13

W         =     33019.272

X         =    0.0043698957

Y         =    0.0012602085

Maximum error is 1.5178830e-18
Warning: floating point overflow

********************************************************************
```

Eureka Quick Reference Table

This appendix provides brief explanations, in alphabetical order, for many of Eureka's features.

Built-in functions

abs(x)	msqrt(x)
atan2($x1,x2$)	ncum(x)
cos(x)	paymt(i,n,pval,fval)
cosh(x)	pi( )
deriv($x1$,x2)	polar($x1,x2$)
exp(x)	poly(x,series)
fact(x)	pos(x)
floor(x)	pval(i,n,paymt,fval)
frac(x)	re(x)
fval(i,n,pval,paymt)	sgn(x)
im(x)	sin(x)
integ(exp,var,$x1,x2 < n >$)	sinh(x)
ln(x)	sqrt(x)
log10(x)	sum(exp,var,x1,x2 $< n >$)
	tan(x)

Calculator operations

Press *C C* to select Calculator from the Commands menu. Press *Num-Lock*, then use the number pad keys located at the right of your keyboard to make entries, then press *Enter*. Eureka works just like a hand-held scientific calculator to solve arithmetic and built-in functions.

| **Default settings** | Change default settings in one of two ways: |

1. Embed directives in the equation file.

2. Change settings from the Options menu:

Press *O S* to select Settings from the Options menu. Scroll through the menu and change the desired settings by pressing *Enter* to toggle between *yes* and *no*, or by entering an appropriate number. Then press *Esc*. Load and save setup files with Load setup and Write setup.

| **Directives** | accuracy, casefold, complex, digits, finanmode, finansmooth, include, initval, listdefault, max, maxtime, min, penalty, plotdefault, radius, rootsign, setting, solve, substlevel, syntax, unit |

| **Directory** | Press *F D* from the main menu, enter optional directory mask, and press *Enter* (* and ? are wildcards). By default, Eureka will list all files in the directory. |

| **Edit an equation file** | Select Edit to input the equation you want to solve. The editor works like the Turbo Pascal and SideKick editors or WordStar in non-document mode. A brief listing of editor commands follows: |

Word left	*Ctrl-Left arrow* or *Ctrl-A*
Word right	*Ctrl-Right arrow* or *Ctrl-F*
Delete character to left	*Backspace*
Delete character under cursor	*Ctrl-G*
Delete word to right of cursor	*Ctrl-T*
Delete line	*Ctrl-Y*
Insert mode on/off	*Ins* or *Ctrl-V*

| **Equation file format** | **Equations**. Equations are written one per line in standard mathematical syntax and notation. Multiplication is not implicit. |

*	multiplication operator
^	exponentiation operator
:=	user-defined functions and initializations
:	used to separate formulas on the same line
_	indicates formula continued on following line

Directives. Directives begin with a dollar sign and follow the general format of the directive shown here:

```
$ digits = 6
```

Comments. Comments must be set off by a semicolon (;) or appear between braces ({ }).

File names

Press *F L* to select Load from the File menu, then enter a file name. File names follow DOS conventions (up to eight characters, and may also include an optional 1 to 3 character extension).

Use the Write to... option on the File menu to make an alternate version of the current file.

Find other roots, modify variables and constants

Press *O V* from the main menu to select Variables from the Options menu. Enter a value, and press *Enter*. Press *Esc* twice to return to the main menu, then choose Iterate from the Command menu to solve for the new variable. In seeking another root, the value should be close to but not greater than that of the second root. Press *Esc*, then press *S* to return to the main menu and Solve.

Function keys

F1	Display help text
F2	Save the current file
F3	New file
F5	Zoom to full screen editor
Alt-F5	Text zoom in plot window
F6	Change active window
F7	Go to active window or block Begin (edit function)
F8	Block end (edit function)
Esc	Select menu
Ctrl-Break	Interrupt solve
Up arrow, Down arrow, Left arrow, Right arrow, PgUp, PgDn,	Move/scroll through the screen
Alt-X	Exit Eureka

List a table of values

Press *G L* from the main menu to select List from the Graph menu. Respond to the prompts by entering the function (if necessary) and the initial value, increment, and number of values; then press *Enter*. See comment under "Plot a graph."

Load a file	Press *F L* from the main menu to select Load from the File menu. At the prompt, type in the name of the file to be loaded; press *Enter*.
Plot a graph	Press *G P* from the main menu to select Plot from the Graph menu. Respond to the prompts by entering the left and right endpoints and then press *Enter*.
	(**Note:** A file must have at least one user-defined function or you must enter one with the Function command before you can select Plot or List.)
Print a report	Press *R O* to select the Output option from the Report menu. Indicate the desired output device and whether you want a formatted header (*Enter* toggles between the various choices). Select Go and press *Enter*.
Quit the program	Press *Q* from the File menu, or press *Alt-X*.
Return to DOS	Press *F O* to select OS Shell from the File menu.
Return to main menu	From a window or submenu, press *Esc*.
Save a file	Press *F S* from the main menu to select Save from the File menu. This saves a copy of your file on your active drive.
Select menu items	**Cursor Method** Move cursor to desired menu item and press *Enter*.
	Initial Letter Method Type the capital letter of the desired option. For example, to select the Calculator option on the Commands menu, you would press *CC*.
Settings	In addition to those listed under "Directives:" list_first, list_num, list_inc, plot_left, plot_right.
Start the program	Log on to the drive or directory containing the program and type EUREKA *Enter*.
Solve a problem	Press *S* from the main menu to select Solve.
	To solve the problem another time, press *C I* from the main menu to select the Iterate command from the Commands menu.
	To look in a different region for an answer, press *C F* from the main menu to select the Find other command from the Commands menu.
Verify a solution	Press *C V* from the main menu to select Verify from the Commands menu.

Eureka Editor Commands

All Eureka editor commands are described in this appendix. Each description consists of:

- a heading defining the command
- the keystrokes that activate the command
- a brief explanation of what the command does

If there are two ways of giving a command, that is, one using the IBM cursor keys and the other using *Ctrl*, both ways are listed, with the IBM cursor key method listed first.

If you are familiar with WordStar or the Turbo Pascal and SideKick editors, you should have no trouble with the Eureka editor, since it is virtually identical to these editors.

For hands-on practice with using the editor, see the tutorials in Chapter 2. To change default editor keystrokes, use the EINST program, described in Appendix F.

Cursor Movement Commands

These commands control the position of the cursor in the file. You can manage fairly well with just the cursor keys and *PgUp* and *PgDn*; the other commands are handy but may not be critical for small files.

Character left   *Left arrow* or *Ctrl-S*
Moves the cursor one character to the left without affecting the character there. This command does not work across line breaks; when the cursor reaches the left edge of the window, it stops.

Character right   *Right arrow* or *Ctrl-D*
Moves the cursor one character to the right without affecting the character there. This command does not work across line breaks; when the cursor reaches the right edge of the window, the text starts scrolling horizontally until the cursor reaches the extreme right of the line in column 250, where it stops.

Line down   *Down arrow* or *Ctrl-X*
Moves the cursor to the line below. If the cursor is on the second-to-the-last line, the window scrolls up one line.

Line up   *Up arrow* or *Ctrl-E*
Moves the cursor up to the line above. If the cursor is on the top line, the window scrolls down one line.

Page down   *PgDn* or *Ctrl-C*
Moves the cursor one page (window) down with an overlap of one line. The cursor moves one window less one line forward in the text.

Page up   *PgUp* or *Ctrl-R*
Moves the cursor one page (window) up with an overlap of one line. The cursor moves one window less one line backward in the text.

To end of file   *Ctrl-PgDn* or *Ctrl-Q C*
Moves the cursor to the last character of the text.

To top of file   *Ctrl-PgUp* or *Ctrl-Q R*
Moves the cursor to the first character of the text.

To last cursor position   *Ctrl-Q P*
Moves the cursor to the last position it occupied. This command is useful, for example, to move back to the last position after a Find/Replace operation.

To left margin   *Home* or *Ctrl-Q S*
Moves the cursor all the way to the left edge of the window (column 1).

To right end of line   *End* or *Ctrl-Q D*
Moves the cursor to the end of the line; in other words, to the position following the last printable character on the line. Trailing blanks are always removed from all lines to save space.

To top of window   *Ctrl-Home* or *Ctrl-Q E*

Moves the cursor to the top of the editor window.

To bottom of window   *Ctrl-End* or *Ctrl-Q X*

Moves the cursor to the bottom of the editor window.

Word left   *Ctrl-Left arrow* or *Ctrl-A*

Moves the cursor to the beginning of the word to the left. A word is defined as a
sequence of characters delimited by one of the following characters: space < > , ;
. ( ) [ ] ^ ' * + − / $.

Word right   *Ctrl-Right arrow* or *Ctrl-F*

Moves the cursor to the beginning of the word to the right. A word is defined as a
sequence of characters delimited by one of the following characters: space < > , ;
. ( ) [ ] ^ ' * + - / $.

Insert and Delete Commands

These commands let you insert and delete text by character, word, and line, and
control the Insert/Overwrite typing mode.

Delete character to left   *Backspace*

This is the backspace key just above *Enter.* It moves one character to the left and
deletes the character there. Any characters to the right of the cursor are moved to
the left.

Delete character under cursor   *Del* or *Ctrl-G*

Deletes the character under the cursor and moves any characters to the right of the
cursor one position to the left. This command does not work across line breaks.

Delete word right   *Ctrl-T*

Deletes the word to the right of the cursor. A word is defined in "Word left" under
cursor movement commands.

Delete to end of line   *Ctrl-Q Y*

Deletes all text from the cursor position right to the end of the line.

Insert mode on/off   *Ins* or *Ctrl-V*

This command lets you switch between insert, the default, and overwrite mode
while entering text. The current mode is displayed on the status line of the editor
window. In Insert mode, new text is tucked in at the cursor position, and existing
text is moved to the right. Overwrite mode is convenient for replacing old text with
new. In this mode, existing characters are replaced by the new characters typed
over them.

Line deletion   *Ctrl-Y*

Deletes the line containing the cursor and moves any lines below one line up. The cursor moves to the left edge of the window. Be careful; there is no way to restore a deleted line.

Line insertion   *Ctrl-N*

Inserts a line break at the cursor position. The cursor remains stationary.

Block Commands

Block commands allow you to maneuver chunks of text. A block can be any amount of text from a single character to an entire file. A block is marked by placing a "begin block" marker before the first character and an "end block" marker after the last character of the desired portion of text. So marked, a block can be copied, moved, deleted, or written as a file.

Block copy   *Ctrl-K C*

Places a copy of a marked block starting at the cursor position. The original block is left unchanged.

Block move   *Ctrl-K V*

Moves a marked block from its original position to the cursor position. The block disappears from its original position.

Block delete   *Ctrl-K Y*

Deletes a marked block. Be careful; no provision exists for restoring a deleted block of text.

Hide/display block   *Ctrl-K H*

This command causes the visual marking of a block to be toggled off and on. The copy, move, delete, and write to a file block manipulation commands work only when the block is visibly marked.

Mark block begin   *Ctrl-K B*

Marks the beginning of a block. The marker itself is not visible on the screen, and the block only becomes visibly marked (displayed in lower-intensity text) when the end block marker is set. You can also use the begin block marker as a reference point in your text and jump directly to it with the *Ctrl-Q B* command.

Mark block end   *Ctrl-K K*

Marks the end of a block. As above, the marker itself is not visible on the screen, and the block only becomes visible after the begin block marker is set. You can also use the begin block marker as a reference point in your text and jump directly to it with the *Ctrl-Q K* command.

Mark single word   *Ctrl-K T*

Mark a single word as a block. If the cursor is placed within a word, the word is marked; if the cursor is not on a word, the word to its left is marked. A word is as defined in "Word left" under cursor commands.

Read block from disk   *Ctrl-K R*

This command is used to read a file into the current text at the cursor position, exactly as if it were a block that was being copied or moved.

Write block to disk   *Ctrl-K W*

This command is used to write a previously marked block to a file. The block is left unchanged, and the markers remain in place. When you use this command, you are prompted for the name of the file to write to. If the file name specified already exists, a warning is given before the existing file is overwritten.

Miscellaneous Editing Commands

Abort operation   *Ctrl-U*

Abort the current editing operation when it pauses for input (for example, when Search and replace asks "Replace Y/N?" or during the entry of a file name for a block read).

Control character prefix   *Ctrl-P*

The editor allows you to enter control characters into the file by prefixing the desired control character with *Ctrl-P*. Control characters are displayed as half-intensity capital letters.

For instance, to cause an Epson printer to print condensed type, enter *Ctrl-P Ctrl-O*. Consult your printer's manual for more information about printing control commands. You can also use *Ctrl-B* (for bold) or *Ctrl-S* (for underline) to emphasize text. These are toggle characters, so you turn off bold, for example, by entering *Ctrl-P Ctrl-B* after the last character that should be printed in bold.

Find   *Ctrl-Q F*

This command lets you search for a string of characters. A prompt appears above the status line, requesting a search string. If you make an error while typing the string, use the Backspace key to back up and correct it. The string may contain any characters, including control characters. Control characters are entered into the search string with the *Ctrl-P* prefix. To find a line break, search for *Ctrl-M Ctrl-J*.

After the search string has been specified, you are asked for search options. Enter the required options (if any), then press *Enter* to start the search. If the text contains a target matching the search string, the cursor is positioned at the end of the target. To repeat the search operation, use the repeat last find command, *Ctrl-L*. The following options are available (and need not be entered in uppercase):

B Search backwards from the current cursor position towards the beginning of the file

n n = an integer. Type the number of occurrences of the string for which the search should take place, counted from the current cursor position.

U Ignore uppercase or lowercase. Regard uppercase and lowercase alphabeticals as equivalent.

W Search for whole words only. Skip matching patterns that are embedded in other words.

Find and replace $\qquad$ *Ctrl-Q A*

This command lets you search for a string of characters, and then replace it with another. A prompt appears above the status line, requesting a search string. A further prompt requests the replacement string. In nearly every other respect, this commands functions like Find, described previously. There are two additional options:

G Global search and replace. Search and replace throughout the entire text, irrespective of the current cursor position.

N Replace without asking. Does not stop and query whether or not the replace should be carried out at every occurrence of the search string.

Page break $\qquad$ *Ctrl-P Ctrl-L*

Inserts a page break (an ASCII form feed) at the cursor position.

Repeat last find $\qquad$ *Ctrl-L*

Repeats the last Find or Find and replace operation exactly as if all the information had been re-entered.

Restore error message $\qquad$ *Ctrl-Q W*

Redisplay last error message.

Restore line $\qquad$ *Ctrl-Q L*

Restores a line to its original state regardless of what changes you have made; however, you cannot have left the line for the command to be effective.

Tab $\qquad$ *Tab or Ctrl-I*

Moves the cursor eight spaces to the right (hard tabs) or moves cursor to next column based on spacing in the line above (soft tabs).

Tab mode toggle $\qquad$ *Ctrl-O T*

Toggles tabs on and off.

Set tab $\qquad$ *Ctrl-O I*

Sets tab at cursor position.

Built-in Functions

Eureka's built-in functions are described in alphabetical order in this appendix. The standard mathematical and other functions are listed below:

Standard Mathematical Functions	Other Functions
abs	deriv
atan2	floor
cos	frac
cosh	fval
exp	im
fact	integ
ln	ncum
log10	paymt
pi ( )	polar
sin	poly
sinh	pos
tan	pval
tanh	re
	sgn
	sqrt
	sum

The following notations are used in describing the functions:

expr   must be an expression
series series of values or expressions
var   variable identifier
x   value or expression

abs   *Absolute Value*   *abs(x)*

This function returns the absolute value of x. If x is positive, x is returned. If x is negative, $-x$ is returned.

Examples

```
abs(5) returns 5
abs(-15.5) returns 15.5
```

atan2   *Arc Tangent*   *atan2(x1,x2)*

This trigonometric function returns the inverse tangent of $x1/x2$. This is the angle, in radians, formed by $x2$ and $x1$. This function offers an extension to the usual Arc Tangent in that it applies to all four quadrants. The rules that one used in determining $\theta = atan2(x1, x2)$ are as follows:

Quadrant
I   if $x1$ and $x2 > 0$, then $0 < \theta < \pi/2$
II   if $x1 > 0$ and $x2 < 0$, then $\pi/2 < \theta < \pi$
III   if $x1$ and $x2 < 0$, then $-\pi < \theta < -\pi/2$
IV   if $x1 < 0$ and $x2 > 0$, then $-\pi/2 < \theta < 0$

The quadrants progress counterclockwise, with I at the upper right-hand corner.

Example

```
atan2(1,-1) returns 2.35619449
```

cos   *Cosine*   *cos(x)*

This trigonometric function returns the cosine of x. x is assumed to be the angle in radians.

Example

```
cos(1) returns 0.54030231
```

cosh   *Hyperbolic Cosine*   *cosh(x)*

This function returns the hyperbolic cosine of x.

Example

```
cosh(2) returns 3.76219569
```

deriv   *Partial Derivative*   *deriv(x1,x2)*

This function returns the partial derivative of the first argument with respect to the second. The second argument must be a variable. For example, solving

```
z = deriv(x^3 + 5 * x,x)
x = 1
```

gives

```
x = 1.00000000
z = 8.00000000
```

The derivative of $x^3 + 5x$ is $3x^2 + 5$, which has the value 8 when $x = 1$. If other variables besides x were to appear in the expression, they would be treated as constants in the derivative to be evaluated. For example, solving

```
z = deriv(x^3 + y^2 + 5 * x,x)
x = 1
y = 2
```

gives

```
x = 1.00000000
y = 2.00000000
z = 8.00000000
```

However, while Eureka makes substitutions internally in order to solve equations, such substitutions do not affect derivatives. For instance, solving

```
y = x^3 + 5 * x
z = deriv(y,x)
x = 1
```

gives

```
x = 1.00000000
y = 6.00000000
z = 0.00000000
```

This result occurs because *deriv* treats x and y as independent variables. To differentiate an expression that occurs frequently, you should define an appropriate function. Here this function could be

```
f(x) : = x^3 + 5 * x
z = deriv(f(x),x)
x = 1
```

gives

```
x = 1.00000000
z = 8.00000000
```

exp   *Exponentiation*   *exp(x)*

This exponential function raises the number e to the power x.

Examples

```
exp(0) returns 1.00000000
exp(1) returns 2.71828183
```

fact   *Factorial*   *fact(x)*

This function calculates the factorial of the positive integer specified by x. The integer x must be less than or equal to 170.

Examples

```
fact(6) returns 720.000000
fact(3) returns 6.00000000
```

floor   *Floor*   *floor(x)*

This function rounds x down to the nearest integer.

Examples

```
floor(-2.5) returns -3.00000000
floor(2.999 + 2.999) returns 5.00000000
```

frac   Fraction   frac(x)

This function returns as a positive number the part of *x* that is not an integer.

Examples

```
frac(2.5) returns 0.50000000
frac(1.33 + 1.55) returns 0.88000000
```

fval   Future Value   fval(i,n,pval,paymt)

This financial function returns the future value of a mortgage or similar contract (the money received at the end of a contract). *n* is normally an integer representing the number of payment intervals; *i* is the interest rate per payment expressed in hundredths; *pval* and *paymt* are described elsewhere in this section. *fval* is either zero or a negative number representing the balloon payment. See page 99 in Chapter 5 for more details.

Example

If you borrow $250,000 at 10% and make ten annual payments of $35,000, how much money do you owe the lender at the end of the contract?

```
fval(0.10,10,250000,-35000) returns -90625.75
```

im   Imaginary Number   im(x)

This function returns the imaginary part of a complex number. (**Note:** The complex number setting must be set to *yes*.)

Example

```
$ complex = yes
im(3 + 2 * sqrt(-1)) returns 2
```

integ   Integral   integ(exp,var,x1,x2 <n>)

This function returns the integral of the first argument with respect to the second. The second argument must be a variable. The third argument is the lower limit of integration, and the fourth argument is the upper limit. Improper integrals are not allowed.

This function returns the definite integral for the variable (*var*) varied in the specified expression between the limits *x*1 and *x*2. *Integ* uses Simpson's Rule to compute the integral. $<n>$ is the number of subdivisions used for the integral. If *n* is not specified, 10 subdivisions are used. (See *deriv* for more discussion of differential calculus.)

Expressions can also be integrated with respect to a given variable. For example, solving

```
z  = integ(sin(x),x,0,pi)
pi = 3.14159265359
```

gives the integral of sin(*x*) as *x* goes from 0 to pi:

```
pi = 3.14159265359
x  = 1.23900000
z  = 2.00000000
```

In this case, the value for *x* is meaningless because it is not subject to any constraints. As with derivatives, variables other than the variables of integration are treated as constants, but functions can be used. The last two arguments to *integ*, lower and upper limits of integration, can be arbitrary expressions.

Example

```
integ(x^2 + 3 * x + 4,x,2,7) = y
```

returns the area under the function $x^2 + 3x + 4$, between

```
x = 2 and x = 7, or y = 199.16666667.
```


ln　　*Natural Logarithm*　　*ln(x)*

This function returns the natural logarithm (base $e = 2.71828183$) of *x*. *x* must be greater than 0.

Examples

```
ln(exp(1)) returns 1
ln(15) returns 2.70805020
```


log10　　*Logarithm base 10*　　*log10(x)*

This function returns the logarithm base 10 of *x*. *x* must be greater than 0.

Example

```
log10(1) = 0
log10(12) = 1.0791812
```

msqrt   *Negative Square Root*   *msqrt(x)*

This function returns the negative (minimum or minus) square root of x.

Example

```
msqrt(9) returns -3
```

ncum   *Normal Cumulative*   *ncum(x)*

This function returns the probability that a normal random variable will be below its mean plus x standard deviations. It can also be expressed as

$$\text{ncum}(x) = \frac{1}{\sqrt{(2\pi)}} \int_{-\infty}^{X} \exp(-t^2/2)\, dt$$

ncum is the basic tool used in analyzing the variance of normal distributions in statistics and probability. The importance of the normal distribution is primarily due to the Central Limit Theorem. This theorem states that any sum of independent random variables approximates a normal random variable, with the approximation becoming more accurate as more variables are summed. In the experimental sciences, the deviation from theory and experiment can be explained as an error which is the sum of error contributions from many sources. The resulting error is usually quite well approximated as a random variable.

As an example of the use of *ncum*, consider a chemist who is measuring pollutants in the air. After taking a number of readings, s/he computes the average pollen concentration at 150 parts per million (ppm), with a standard deviation of 10 ppm. The probability of making a reading less than 170 ppm is *ncum*(+2), since 170 is 2 standard deviations above 150. Also, the chemist can be very confident that a reading will be less than $150 + 10x$ where

$$\text{ncum}(x) = 0.99$$

Example

```
ncum(1) returns 0.84134456
```

paymt   *Payment*   *paymt(i,n,pval,fval)*

This financial function returns the payment on a mortgage or similar contract. *n* is normally an integer representing the number of payment intervals; *i* is the interest rate per payment expressed in hundredths; *pval* and *fval* are described elsewhere in this section. See the section on financial functions in Chapter 5 for more details.

pi   *pi*   *pi ( )*

This function returns the value of pi (3.14159265359)

polar   *Polar Coordinate*   *polar(x1,x2)*

This function returns the angle in the rectangular to polar coordinate conversion in radians. The conversion

$$x = r \times \cos(\text{theta})$$
$$y = r \times \sin(\text{theta})$$

is inverted by

$$r = \text{sqrt}(x^2 + y^2)$$
$$\text{theta} = \text{polar}(x,y)$$

except for the restriction

$$- \pi < \text{theta} < \pi$$
$$\pi = 3.14159265359$$

If z is complex, these transformations are equivalent to

$$x \quad = \text{re}(z)$$
$$y \quad = \text{im}(z)$$
$$r \quad = \text{abs}(z)$$
$$\text{theta} = \text{im}(\ln(z))$$

Polar(x,y) is the same as the Fortran function atan2(y,x), and is the same as the arc tangent of y/x with the quadrant chosen carefully (see *arctan2* for more details).

Example

```
polar(-1,0) returns 3.14159265
```

poly   *Polynomial*   *poly(x,series)*

This function returns the value of the polynomial of x using the specified series of coefficients. Coefficients are listed in descending order of the variable exponent. For example, the following polynomial equation

$$x^4 + 3x^3 - x^2 + 2x + 1$$

would be expressed as follows:

```
p(x) := poly(x, 1, 3, -1, 2, 1)
```

Applying Solve to a file containing *poly* causes Eureka to find all the roots, as well as solve for whatever other variables are in the file.

A root to a polynomial is a complex number that yields zero when plugged into the polynomial. A polynomial of degree n always has exactly n roots, counting repetitions. Since the polynomial here has real coefficients, the roots are either real or occur in complex conjugate pairs. The above polynomial has the following roots:

No.	Real Part	Imaginary
1	−0.29105149	0.00000000
2	0.50677653	1.00258931
3	0.50677653	−1.00258931
4	−2.72250157	0.00000000

pos   *Positive*   *pos(x)*

This function returns the positive value of x.

Examples

```
pos(1.2) returns 1.20000000
pos(-12) returns 0.00000000
```

pval　　*Present Value*　　*pval(i,n,paymt,fval)*

This financial function returns the present value on a mortgage or similar contract. (For a mortgage, this is the amount of the loan minus the down payment.) n is normally an integer representing the number of payment intervals; i is the interest rate per payment expressed in hundredths; *paymt* and *fval* are described elsewhere in this section. See page 99 in Chapter 5 for more details.

re　　*Real Number*　　*re(x)*

This function returns the real part of a complex number. (**Note:** Complex numbers must be set to *yes*.)

Example

```
$ complex = yes
re(3 + 2 * sqrt(-1) returns 3
```

sgn　　*Sign*　　*sgn(x)*

This function returns 1 if $x > 0$ or if $x = 0$; otherwise, it returns -1 if $x < 0$.

Examples

```
sgn(10) returns 1
sgn(0) returns 1
sgn(-1) returns -1
```

sin　　*Sine*　　*sin(x)*

This trigonometric function returns the sine of x. x is the angle in radians.

Example

```
sin(1) returns 0.84147098
```

sinh   *Hyperbolic Sine*   *sinh(x)*

This function returns the hyperbolic sine of *x*.

Example

    sinh(1) returns 1.17520119

sqrt   *Square Root*   *sqrt(x)*

This function returns the positive square root of the argument *x*.

Example

    sqrt(81) returns 9.00000000

sum   *Sum*   *sum(exp,var,x1,x2)*

This function returns the sum of the series defined by replacing the variable in the second argument in the function of the first argument over the range expressed in the third and fourth arguments, or

$$\sum_{x=1}^{n} f(x)$$

where $f(x) = $ exp
$\quad x = $ var
$\quad 1 = x1$
$\quad n = x2$

The second argument must be a variable. The third argument is the lower limit of the summation, and the fourth argument is the upper limit.

Example

    sum(4 * x,x,1,3) returns 24

tan   *Tangent*   *tan(x)*

This trigonometric function returns the tangent of x, where x is an angle measured in radians.

Examples

```
tan(0)  returns 0.00000000
tan(1)  returns 1.55740772
```

tanh   *Hyperbolic Tangent*   *tanh(x)*

This trigonometric function returns the hyperbolic tangent of x.

Example

```
tanh(1)  returns 0.76159416
```

A DOS Primer

If you are new to computers or to DOS, you may have trouble understanding certain terms used in this manual. This appendix provides you with a brief overview of the following DOS concepts and functions:

- What DOS is and does
- The proper way to load a program
- Directories, subdirectories, and the path command
- Using AUTOEXEC.BAT files

This information is by no means a complete explanation of the DOS operating system. If you need more details, please refer to the MS-DOS™ or PC-DOS™ user's manual that came with your computer system.

Eureka runs under the MS-DOS or PC-DOS operating system, version 2.0 or later.

What Is DOS?

DOS is shorthand for Disk Operating System. MS-DOS is Microsoft's version of DOS, while PC-DOS is IBM's rendition. DOS is the traffic coordinator, manager, and operator for the transactions that occur between the parts of the computer system and the computer system and you. DOS operates in the background, taking care of many of the menial computer tasks you wouldn't want to have to think about—for instance, the flow of characters between your keyboard and the computer, between the computer and your printer, and between your disk(s) and internal memory (RAM).

Other DOS transactions are ones that you initiate by entering commands on the DOS command line; in other words, immediately after the DOS prompt. Your DOS prompt looks like one of the following:

```
A>
B>
C>
```

The capital letter refers to the active disk drive (the one DOS and you are using right now). For instance, if the prompt is A>, it means you are working with the files on drive A, and that commands you give DOS will refer to this drive. When you want to switch to another disk, making it the active disk, all you do is type the letter of the disk, followed by a colon and *Enter*. For instance, to switch to drive B, just type B:*Enter*.

There are a few commands that you will use often with DOS, if you haven't already, such as

DEL or ERASE	To erase a file
DIR	To see a list of files on the logged disk
COPY	To copy files from one disk to another
EUREKA	To load Eureka: The Solver

DOS doesn't care whether you type in uppercase or lowercase letters, or a combination of both, so you can enter your commands however you like.

We'll assume you know how to use the first three commands listed; if you don't, refer to your DOS manual. Next, we will explain the proper way to load a program like Eureka: The Solver, and that involves the last command—EUREKA.

How to Load a Program

On your distribution disk, you'll find the main Eureka program, under the file name EUREKA.EXE. This program file is necessary for all functions, so you always need it when you first start the program. A file name with the "last name" or extension .COM or .EXE means a program file that you can load and run (use) by typing only its "first name" on the DOS command line. So, to invoke Eureka, you simply type EUREKA and press *Enter*, and Eureka will be loaded into your computer's memory.

There's one thing you need to remember about loading Eureka and other similar programs: *You must be logged onto the disk and directory where the program is located in order to load it*; otherwise, unless you have set up a DOS path (described shortly), DOS won't know where to find the program. (In DOS 3.0, however, you can load a program by giving the full path name.)

For instance, if your distribution disk with the EUREKA.EXE program is in drive A but the prompt you see on your screen is B>, DOS won't know what you're talking about if you type EUREKA and press *Enter*, and will give you the message "Bad command or file name."

It's as if you were shuffling through the "School Records" file in your file cabinet looking for information about your home finances. You're in the wrong place. So if you happen to get that DOS message, simply switch to drive A by typing A: and then press *Enter*. Then type EUREKA and press *Enter* to load Eureka.

You can set up a "path" to the Eureka files so that DOS can find them, using the DOS *path* command. See the section on the AUTOEXEC.BAT file for more information.

Directories

A *directory* is a convenient way to organize your floppy or hard disk files. Directories allow you to subdivide your disk into sections, much the way you might put groups of manila file folders into separate file boxes. For instance, you might want to put all your file folders having to do with finance — for instance, a bank statement file, an income tax file, or the like — into a box labeled "Finances."

On your computer, it would be convenient to make a directory to hold all your Eureka files, another for your SideKick files, another for your letters, and so on. That way, when you type DIR on the DOS command line, you don't have to wade through hundreds of file names looking for the file you want. You'll get a listing of only the files on the directory you're currently logged onto.

Although you can make directories on either floppy or hard disks, they are used most often on hard disks. This is because a hard disk can hold a greater volume of data, so there is a greater need for organization and compartmentalization.

When you're at the DOS level, rather than in Eureka or another program, you can tell DOS to create directories, move files around between directories, and display which files are in a particular directory.

In the examples that follow, we assume you are using a hard disk system, and that you are logged on to the hard disk so that the prompt you see on your screen is C>. If you want to create directories on your floppy disks, just substitute A or B

To make a directory for your Eureka files, do the following:

1. At the C> prompt, type MKDIR EUREKA and press *Enter*. The MKDIR command tells DOS to make a directory called EUREKA.

2. Type CHDIR EUREKA and press *Enter*. The CHDIR command tells DOS to move you into the EUREKA directory.

3. Now, put the Eureka disk you want to copy from into one of your floppy drives—let's say A for this example—and type COPY A:*.* *Enter*. (The asterisks are *wildcards* that stand for all files.) The COPY command tells DOS to copy all files on the A drive to the EUREKA directory on the C drive. As each file on the disk is copied, you will see it listed on the screen.

That's all there is to it. Treat a directory the same way you would a disk drive: To load Eureka, you must be in the EUREKA directory before typing Eureka and pressing *Enter*, or DOS won't be able to find the program.

Subdirectories

If you are someone who really likes organization, you can further subdivide your directories into subdirectories. You can create as many directories and subdirectories as you like—just don't forget where you put your files!

A subdirectory is created the same way as a directory. To create a subdirectory from the EUREKA directory (for instance, for storing your equation files), do the following:

1. Be sure you are in the EUREKA directory.

2. Type MKDIR FILES *Enter*.

3. Type CHDIR FILES. You are now in the FILES subdirectory.

4. Copy your equation files to the new subdirectory.

If you do put your files in a subdirectory, you can let Eureka know where they are by using the EINST program (see Appendix F).

Where Am I? The $p $g Prompt

You probably have noticed that when you change directories, you still see the C> prompt; there is no evidence of what directory or subdirectory you are in. This can be confusing, especially if you leave your computer for a while. It's easy to forget where you were when you left.

DOS gives you an easy way to find out. Just type

```
prompt=$p $g
```

and from now on (until you turn your computer off or reboot), the prompt will show you exactly where you are. Try it. If you are still in the FILES subdirectory, your DOS prompt should look like

```
C:\EUREKA\FILES >
```

The AUTOEXEC.BAT File

To avoid typing the prompt command (discussed in the previous section) to see "where you are" every time you turn on your computer, you can set up an AUTOEXEC.BAT file to do it for you each time you turn on your computer.

The AUTOEXEC.BAT file is a useful tool to set your computer to do things automatically. There are many more things it can do, but rather than go into great detail here, we suggest referring to your DOS manual for more information. We will show you how to create an AUTOEXEC.BAT file that will automatically change your prompt so you know where you are in your directory structure, set a *path* to the Eureka directory, and change to the EUREKA directory.

The DOS *path* command tells your computer where to look for commands it doesn't recognize. DOS only recognizes programs in the current (logged) directory, unless there is a path to the directory containing pertinent programs or files. In the following example, we will set a path to the EUREKA directory.

If you have an AUTOEXEC.BAT file in your root directory, your computer will do everything in that file when you first turn your computer on. (The root directory is where you see the C > or C:\ prompt, with no directory names following it.)

Here's how to create an AUTOEXEC.BAT file.

1. Type CHDIR \ *Enter* to get to the root directory.
2. Type COPY CON AUTOEXEC.BAT *Enter.* This tells DOS to copy whatever you type next into a file called AUTOEXEC.BAT.
3. Type

    ```
    PROMPT=$P $G
    PATH=C:\EUREKA
    CHDIR EUREKA
    Ctrl-Z
    ```

The *Ctrl-Z* sequence saves your commands in the AUTOEXEC.BAT file.

To test your new AUTOEXEC.BAT file, reboot your computer by holding down the *Ctrl* and *Alt* keys and then pressing *Del*. You should see C:\EUREKA > .

Changing Directories

How do you get from one directory to another? It depends on where you want to go. The basic DOS command for changing directories is CHDIR. Use it like this:

- *To move from one directory to another*: For example, to change from the EUREKA directory to one called WP, type the following from the EUREKA directory:

    `C:\EUREKA> CHDIR \WP` *Enter*

    Notice the backslash (\) before the directory name. Whenever you are moving from one directory to another unrelated directory, type the name of the directory, preceded by a backslash.

- *To move from a directory to its subdirectory*: For example, to move from the EUREKA directory to the FILES subdirectory, type the following from the EUREKA directory:

    `C:\EUREKA> CHDIR FILES` *Enter*

    In this case, you did not need the backslash, because the FILES directory is a direct offshoot of the EUREKA directory. In fact, DOS would have misunderstood what you meant if you had used the backslash in this case. If you had included the backslash, DOS would have thought that FILES was a directory off the main (root) directory.

- *To move from a subdirectory to its parent directory*: For example, to move from the FILES subdirectory to the EUREKA directory, type the following from the FILES subdirectory:

    `C:\EUREKA\FILES> CHDIR ..` *Enter*

    DOS will move you back to the EUREKA directory. Any time you want to move back to the parent directory, type two periods after the CHDIR command.

- *To move to the root directory*: The *root directory* is the original directory. It is the parent (or grandparent) of all directories (and subdirectories). When you are in the root directory, you see this prompt: C:\ > .

    To move to the root directory from any other directory, simply type

    `CHDIR \` *Enter*

    The backslash without a directory name signals DOS that you want to return to the root directory.

This appendix has presented only a quick look at DOS and some of its functions. Once you're familiar with the information given here, you may want to study your DOS manual and discover the many things you can do with your computer's operating system. There are many other DOS functions not mentioned here that can simplify and enhance your computer use.

Eureka: The Solver Owner's Handbook

Error Messages

The various error messages you may encounter while using Eureka are described in alphabetical order in this appendix. These messages appear in the Error window. When applicable, a line reference may also appear with the error message. The line reference specifies the line in the equation file that contains the error. However, when you use the Calculator, only the word ERROR appears, although the cause of the problem may be one described in this appendix.

Assignment Must Be to a Variable or Function

Cause: Syntax problem. Attempting to solve an equation file in which an assignment (using : =) has been made to something other than a recognizable variable or function.

Solution: Edit the file to provide a legitimate variable or function, as required.

Bad Function Call

Cause: Internal error. Generated if Eureka attempts to solve an incorrectly defined function.

Solution: Quit Eureka, then reactivate it.

Cannot Complexify Floor or Frac

Cause: Setting error. The active equation file includes the *floor* or *frac* function, but either the complex setting or *complex* directive has been set to *yes*.

Solution: Change the setting or directive to *no*.

Cannot Have Complex Derivatives or Integrals

Cause: Setting error. The active equation file includes the *deriv* or *integ* function, but either the complex setting or *complex* directive has been set to *yes*.

Solution: Change the setting or directive to *no*.

Circular Function Definition

Cause: Attempting to solve an equation file that contains a tautological function definition; that is, one that does not produce an assignable value. An example of this is:

```
f(x) := x^2 + 3 * g(x)
g(x) := f(x + 1) - 7 * x
```

Solution: Rewrite the incorrect definition.

Comma Expected

Cause: Syntax problem. In attempting to solve the equation file, Eureka has encountered an equation that lacks one or more commas between values or constants that are function arguments.

Solution: Edit the equation so that it contains the correct number of commas.

Command Not Understood

Cause: Syntax error. In attempting to solve an equation file, Eureka has encountered an unintelligible directive (to the left of the equal sign); for example:

    $ ccomplex = yes

Solution: Restore the directive to its proper form:

    $ complex = yes

Constant Expected

Cause: Attempting to solve an equation file in which something other than a recognizable constant appears where one is syntactically expected.

Solution: Edit the file to provide a legitimate constant.

Dynamic Memory Depleted

Cause: Memory problem. The area allocated to Eureka has been filled.

Solution: Quit Eureka, then reactivate it.

Equations are Inconsistent

Cause: Attempting to solve an equation file in which the equations do not follow the correct sequence.

Solution: Edit the equations so they follow the correct syntax.

File Already Exists

Cause: In using the Rename command, you have entered a file name that already exists.

Solution: Select Rename again, but enter a name not currently in use.

File Not Found

Cause: In attempting to use Load to bring a file to the screen, no file name has been found to match the one entered.

Solution: Doublecheck the file name and try again, remembering extensions.

File Too Large

Cause: Attempting to use Save on a file that will not fit in the available disk space.

Solution: Cut down the size of the file, or if possible, save to another memory device (such as a different data disk).

Function is Multiply Defined

Cause: Syntax error. Attempting to solve an equation file in which the same function definition is used more than once. For example:

```
f(a) := pos(x + y)
f(b) := pos(z)
```

Solution: Edit the equation file to eliminate redundant version(s) of the function definition:

```
f(a) := pos(x + y)
g(b) := pos(z)
```

Function is Undefined

Cause: Syntax problem. Attempting to solve an equation file that contains an equation with an undefined function.

Solution: Edit the equation so that it contains an appropriate built-in function or correctly stated user-defined function.

Identifier Expected

Cause: Syntax problem. Attempting to solve an equation file that lacks a variable name where one should syntactically appear.

Solution: Edit the file to include the necessary character.

Identifier Too Long

Cause: A variable name is too long.

Solution: Edit the file to eliminate redundant characters or recast the formula as necessary.

Incorrect Number of Function Arguments

Cause: Syntax problem. Attempting to solve an equation file that contains a function with a different number of arguments than those indicated in the function definition.

Solution: Edit the function to contain the correct number of arguments.

Invalid Function Argument

Cause: Attempting to solve an equation file containing a function with an improper argument. For example, replacing either of the plus signs in this equation with an equal sign:

```
frac(x + 2.5 + 0.33).
```

Solution: Edit the necessary function arguments.

Invalid Function Definition

Cause: Syntax problem. Attempting to solve an equation file that contains an improperly defined function, such as a numeral appearing between the parentheses.

Solution: Edit the function definition so that it is properly formed.

Invalid Number

Cause: In attempting to solve the equation file, Eureka has encountered an illegal symbolic value. For instance, while *e* (indicating scientific notation) is allowed, it may be entered incorrectly.

Solution: Edit the equation file so that it contains a legal symbolic value.

Memory Heap Overflow

Cause: Attempting to solve an equation file that contains an equation requiring more memory than is available in RAM on your computer.

Solution: Recast the equation or get more RAM for your computer.

Must Differentiate With Respect to a Variable

Cause: Attempting to solve an equation file that uses the *deriv* function incorrectly.

Solution: Recast the *deriv* function.

Numeral or Operator Expected

Cause: Attempting to solve an equation file that contains something other than a numeral or operator where, syntactically, one should appear.

Solution: Edit the file to correct the character(s).

Polynomial is Invalid

Cause: An internal error is generated if Eureka attempts to solve an invalid polynomial.

Solution: Exit Eureka, then reactivate it.

Printer Not Ready

Cause: Hardware problem. In attempting to use the Report Go command to print a report, some difficulty with the printer has been encountered.

Solution: Check that the printer is on, select is on, ribbon and paper are properly feeding and in place, cables are tight, and so on.

Quote Mark Expected

Cause: Syntax error. Attempting to solve an equation file that lacks a quotation mark where one should appear around a file name specified by the *include* directive.

Solution: Edit the file to insert the necessary quotation mark.

Relational Operator Expected

Cause: Syntax error. In attempting to solve the equation file, Eureka has encountered an equation lacking an expected relational operator ($<$ or $>$).

Solution: Edit the incomplete equation so that it contains such a relational operator.

Second Argument Must Be a Variable

Cause: Attempting to solve an equation file containing a function in which the second argument must be a variable (such as *deriv* or *integ*) but is not.

Solution: Recast the function argument as a variable.

String Space Overflow

Cause: The memory area allocated to storing strings is full.

Solution: Quit Eureka, then reactivate it.

Sum is Invalid

Cause: Internal error. In attempting to solve the *sum* function, Eureka has encountered an internal problem.

Solution: Quit Eureka, then reactivate it.

Sum is Too Large

Cause: Attempting to solve for the *sum* function when the spread between the initial and final endpoints overtaxes Eureka's internal capacity.

Solution: Recast the function.

Syntax Error for Unit Conversion

Cause: Attempting to solve an equation file that contains an incorrectly formulated unit conversion.

Solution: Reformulate the incorrect syntax.

Too Few Arguments to Poly

Cause: Syntax problem. Attempting to solve an equation file that includes the *poly* function but with only one argument (minimum requirement is two arguments).

Solution: Edit the function to contain the correct number of arguments.

Too Many Active Variables

Cause: Attempting to solve an equation file having more than twenty active variables.

Solution: Recast the file so that it contains twenty or fewer active variables.

Too Many Constants

Cause: Attempting to solve an equation file that causes Eureka to handle more than 200 constants. While an equation file may have only a relatively small number of constants, the solving process itself may sometimes cause Eureka to generate a large number of internal substitution constants and thus cause this message to appear.

Solution: Set the *substlevel* setting to 0.

Too Many Formulas

Cause: Attempting to solve an equation file with more than twenty equations.

Solution: Recast the equation file so that it contains no more than twenty equations. **Note:** Solving in complex mode causes Eureka to actually handle three times the number of equations that appear in the file: the original equation, one for imaginary numbers, and one for real numbers.

Too Many Functions

Cause: Attempting to solve an equation file with more than ten user-defined functions.

Solution: Recast the file so that it contains ten or fewer functions.

Too Many Unit Conversions

Cause: Attempting to solve an equation file having more than ten unit conversions.

Solution: Recast the file so that it contains ten or fewer such conversions.

Too Many Variables

Cause: Attempting to solve an equation file having more than twenty variables.

Solution: Recast the file so that it contains twenty or fewer variables.

Unable to Create File

Cause: Attempting to use Edit to start a new file when, for any of a number of reasons (for example, the data disk is read-only), this is impossible.

Solution: Ascertain the reason for the failure, then use Edit again.

Unexpected End of File

Cause: Attempting to solve an equation file in which the expected terminating character (for example, a closing }) is missing.

Solution: Edit the file to supply a recognizable termination character.

Unexpected $ End Directive

Cause: Attempting to solve an equation file that includes an *end* directive where, syntactically, one should not appear.

Solution: Edit the file to reposition the *end* directive.

Unmatched Parentheses

Cause: Syntax problem. Attempting to solve an equation file containing an expression or comment that lacks either an initial or terminal parenthesis or curly bracket.

Solution: Edit the file so that all parenthetical expressions are correctly enclosed by a pair of symbols.

Unrecognized Character

Cause: Attempting to solve an equation file that contains a character other than a letter, identifier, operator, or numeral in a position where it might be something other than part of a variable name or comment.

Solution: Edit the file to supply a recognizable character.

Unrecognized Setting Value

Cause: Attempting to solve an equation file in which a directive appears that assigns an unknown setting value (for example, $ initval $ = four, where a numeral is expected).

Solution: Edit the directive to include a legitimate setting value ($ initval $ = 4).

Use of Uninitialized Variable

Cause: Syntax problem. Attempting to solve an equation file in which no assignment of a value (using :=) has been made to a variable that must be initialized.

Solution: Edit the file to provide an appropriate initialization.

Variable Expected

Cause: Attempting to solve an equation file that contains something other than an identifiable variable where, syntactically, one should appear.

Solution: Edit the file to correct the erroneous variable.

Variable Has Not Been Initialized

Cause: Syntax problem. The active equation file contains a variable that has not been properly initialized.

Solution: Edit the file so that the variable is initialized.

Customizing Eureka

The program EINST.COM lets you do four things:

- set up a path to your help and setup files
- customize your keyboard to use with Eureka's editor
- modify the default edit modes
- set the screen mode (default, color, black and white, or monochrome)

If you want to store your help (HELP.EKA) and/or setup (INITIAL.EKA— created with Write setup on the Options menu) files on a directory other than the one where you have EUREKA.EXE, or if you are running DOS 2.0, you will need to use the Eureka directory option to set a path to those files.

If you don't like Eureka's default editor keystrokes, or if you want the Eureka editor to behave more like your own text editor, you can use the Text editor command option to customize the editor keystrokes to your liking.

Finally, you can use the Default editor mode option to set several defaults for the editor: insert or overwrite mode, tabs, and autoindenting.

Running EINST

To get started, type EINST at the DOS prompt. The first menu lets you select Eureka directory, Text editor commands, Default edit modes, or Quit. You can either press the highlighted capital letter of the option you want, or use the Up and Down arrow keys to move to your selection and then press *Enter*. For instance, press *D* to modify the **D**efault edit modes. Pressing *Esc* will eventually return you to the main screen.

The Eureka Directory Option

The Eureka directory option is really only useful for hard disk users. You'll use this option to specify a path to your help and setup files (HELP.EKA and INITIAL. EKA), so that they will be accessible from wherever you call up Eureka. (INITIAL. EKA is the file created when you select Write setup from the Options menu.)

When you select the Eureka directory option, you're prompted to enter the full path to the directory where you are storing your files. For example, if you want to keep the files in a subdirectory off a directory called EUREKA, you might type for your path name

```
C:\EUREKA\FILES
```

After entering a path, press *Enter* to accept it and the main menu will redisplay. When you exit the program, you're prompted whether or not to save the changes. Once you save the path, the location is written to disk. (Note that the status line at the bottom of the screen tells you which keystrokes to use when you're in this screen.)

The Text Editor Command Option

This option allows you to change the default keys that you use while in the Eureka editor. Press *T* to modify the editor commands. The help line at the top of the screen shows you which keys to use to move around and make changes. Most of these commands are simply cursor movement commands; however, the **R** option is useful if you make a lot of changes, then decide you want to restore the keystrokes to their factory defaults.

Notice that you can only modify the secondary, or highlighted, keystrokes; the other keystrokes cannot be changed.

To change a keystroke, move the selection bar to the key you want to change, then press *Enter*. You'll then see a selection bar next to the command you want to redefine. Press the key(s) you want to use. If you take another look at the top of the screen, you'll see the help line now lists the available commands:

```
← backspace  C clear  R restore  ↵ accept edit  <Scroll Lock> literal
```

Use the *Backspace* key to backspace and/or delete something in the keystroke box. The **C** option clears, or erases, the whole box. Use **R** to restore the original keystrokes before exiting from the screen. Press *Enter* to accept the keystroke modification you've made. And finally, the < **Scroll Lock** > is a toggle that lets you alternate between command and literal modes.

To explain the < **Scroll Lock** > option, let's take a look at the *Enter* key, which is used to modify and accept the editing of a key command. But suppose you want to change the Find String command from < CtrlQ > < CtrlF > to < CtrlQ > < Enter >. To do so, you would have to toggle *Scroll-Lock* to literal mode, so that when you press the *Enter* key, it will be interpreted literally as part of the new keystroke you are entering. Follow these steps:

1. Make sure < **Scroll Lock** > is toggled to command mode (check the upper right-hand corner of your screen).

2. Then press *Enter* at the Find String command line.

3. Press *Backspace* to delete the < CtrlF > part of the string.

4. Now toggle *Scroll-Lock* > to literal and press *Enter*.

5. Again, toggle *Scroll-Lock* to command mode and then press *Enter* to accept.

After you've defined a new keystroke(s) for a command, press *Enter* to accept it. If you're finished making changes, press *Esc* to exit. If you still have more changes to make, use the arrow keys to scroll up and down the list and select your next command. At this point, if you've accidentally assigned a keystroke sequence that's been used as a control character sequence in the primary command column, the message

```
Command conflicts need to be corrected. Press Esc
```

will flash across the screen. Any duplicated sequences will be highlighted, so you can easily search for any disallowed items and reselect a sequence. If you change your mind, you can use the **R** option to restore the factory default key definitions.

The Default Edit Mode Option

Press **D** to bring up the **D**efault edit modes menu. There are three editor modes that can be installed: **I**nsert mode, **A**utoindent mode, and **T**abs.

Use this menu to set the editor's modes to the settings you prefer. You'll still be able to toggle them ON/OFF from inside the editor; this menu is used to determine whether they *start* ON or OFF when you first load Eureka.

With Insert mode on, anything you enter at the keyboard is inserted at the cursor position, pushing any text to the right of the cursor further right. Toggling Insert mode off allows you to overwrite text at the cursor.

With Autoindent mode on, the cursor returns to the starting column of the previous line. When toggled off, the cursor always returns to column one.

Toggle on Tab mode when you want to insert tabs; toggle off and the tab is automatically set to the beginning of the first word in the previous line.

When you load Eureka, the default values for all three modes are on. You can change the defaults to suit your preferences and save them back to Eureka. Of course, you'll still be able to toggle these modes from inside Eureka's editor.

Either use the arrow keys to move the selection bar to the option and then press *Enter* or else press the key that corresponds to the highlighted capital letter of the option.

The Screen Mode Option

Press **S** to select Screen mode from the installation menu. A pull-down menu will appear from which you can select the screen mode Eureka will use during operation. Your options include

- **Default**
- **Color**
- **B**lack and white
- **Monochrome**

Default Display Mode

By default, Eureka will always operate in the mode that is active when you load it.

Color Display Mode

Eureka will use color mode with 80 × 25 characters no matter what mode is active, switching back to the active mode when you exit.

Black and White Display Mode

Eureka will use black and white mode with 80 × 25 characters no matter what mode is active, switching back to the active mode when you exit.

Monochrome Display Mode

Eureka will use monochrome mode no matter what mode is active, switching back to the active mode when you exit.

Quitting the Program

Once you have finished making all desired changes, select Quit (or press *Esc*) at the main menu. The message "Save changes to EUREKA.EXE?" will appear at the bottom of the screen. If you press *Y* (for Yes), all of the changes you have made will be permanently installed into Eureka. (Of course, you can always run this program again if you want to change them.) If you press *N* (for No), your changes will be ignored and you will be returned to the DOS prompt.

If you decide you want to restore the original Eureka factory defaults, simply copy EUREKA.EXE from your master disk onto your work disk.

Glossary

absolute value: The value of a positive or negative number when the sign has been removed. For instance, the absolute value of both -2 and $+2$ is 2.

argument: A variable or expression representing a value in the definition of a built-in or user-defined function.

comment: In Eureka, statements used to help you identify or document various equation file components. Comments are set off by a semicolon (;) or are enclosed in curly brackets ({like this}); Eureka ignores comments when solving an equation file.

confidence level: A rating that appears in the Solution window when Eureka solves a minimization or maximization problem. The confidence level reveals the degree of certainty Eureka feels about the found solution.

constraint: A condition that must be met for an equation to be satisfactorily solved. The *accuracy* and *penalty* settings can alter the relative strength of a constraint.

default: The value or instruction Eureka uses until you enter a different value. For example, Eureka automatically solves a variable to eight decimal places; that is the default value. You can change selected default values that are listed in the main menu's Options pull-down menu. You can change nearly all the defaults by including a directive in the equation file.

directive: A command to Eureka, embedded within an equation file, that affects only that file. For example, $ complex = yes means variables are solved for as complex numbers.

equation file: The file that contains the problem to be solved. It must contain an equation or inequality and, where pertinent, initialization values and user-defined functions. It may also include directives and comments.

error message: A message that appears in the error message window on the Eureka screen if you type something that is incorrect or inappropriate. Appendix E lists Eureka's error messages and describes how to correct or avoid errors.

file name extension: An optional 1 to 3 character extension to a file name. As shown in these examples, a period separates the file name and the extension: FINANCE.TOM, FORMULA.1, and FORMULA.165. Extensions are convenient for identifying different file versions, or for identifying file ownership.

floating-point error: A warning message that may appear when Eureka has solved for an extremely large number or when a number is divided by zero. It does not necessarily mean the solution is erroneous.

header: A standardized format for the information appearing at the beginning of a Eureka report. The Eureka report headers include the date, time, and file name.

help message: A message that appears in the Help window when you press *FI*. Help messages explain the current area of the program, whether it is a highlighted menu item, window, or other Eureka feature.

identifier: Name for a variable.

initialization: The process of setting initial values for variables or the starting point of an iterative search. Initializations are flagged with the symbol : = .

list: A table of values for a function, generated with Eureka's Graph/List command.

mask: A way to search selectively for a file. In Eureka, wildcard characters (both the asterisk (*) and question mark (?)) are used in combination with fragments of file names as masks. The asterisk finds all character strings starting from the position of the wildcard character; the ? finds only single characters.

math co-processor: A peripheral chip that is used in PCs to speed up mathematical operations.

path name: A listing of the complete DOS path to a particular file, starting with the root directory and including all directories leading up to the file. For example, the path name \TOM\FINANCE\PROB.21 refers to a file called PROB.21 that is located in the finance directory. The finance directory is, in turn, a subdirectory of TOM, which is a subdirectory of the root directory (\).

Progress window: A window that opens when you select Solve. It displays the amount of time the program is taking to find the solution, the current amount of error, and the current solution. When Eureka finds a solution, the Progress window disappears and the Solution window opens.

RAM disk: A software program that causes a definable portion of RAM memory to be treated as an additional disk drive (usually D:).

report file: A Eureka file that contains a report about an equation file. Such a file can be edited using the Eureka editor, but cannot be solved.

Solution window: A window that displays the values Eureka has found for the indicated variables, as well as a rating expressing the degree of confidence Eureka has in the solution(s).

status line: The line at the bottom of the program screen that provides information about the special function keys that are currently available.

steepest descent method: A method of minimizing functions that starts at an initial point and proceeds along a path that is always in the direction of the most rapid decrease for the function.

user-defined function: A one-variable function defined by the user in an equation file or with the Graph Function command. Such a function is essential for a plot to be generated.

verify window: Displays the results of evaluating both sides of the equations in a file separately, and then comparing the results. Eureka must solve an equation file before it can evaluate it.

Eureka: The Solver Owner's Handbook

Software

For the dealer nearest you
or to order by phone
Call (800) 543-7543

4585 Scotts Valley Drive
Scotts Valley, CA 95066

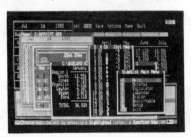
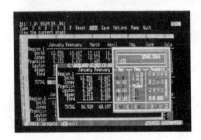

Traveling SIDEKICK®

The Organizer For The Computer Age!

Traveling SideKick is *BinderWare,* both a binder you take with you when you travel and a software program—which includes a Report Generator—that *generates* and *prints out* all the information you'll need to take with you.

Information like your phone list, your client list, your address book, your calendar, and your appointments. The appointment or calendar files you're already using in your SideKick® can automatically be used by your Traveling SideKick. You don't waste time and effort reentering information that's already there.

One keystroke prints out a form like your address book. No need to change printer paper;

you simply punch three holes, fold and clip the form into your Traveling SideKick binder, and you're on your way. Because Traveling SideKick is CAD (Computer-Age Designed), you don't fool around with low-tech tools like scissors, tape, or staples. And because Traveling SideKick is electronic, it works this year, next year, and all the "next years" after that. Old-fashioned daytime organizers are history in 365 days.

What's inside Traveling SideKick

TABLET OF EXTRA FORMS
IN POCKET ON BACK FLAP, FOR USE IN ANY OF THE ORGANIZER SECTIONS.

ADDRESS BOOK SECTION
PREPRINTED ADDRESS FORMS WITH TABBED DIVIDERS FOR EASY REFERENCE.

MISCELLANEOUS SECTION
TO STORE ALL EXTRA PREPRINTED FORMS AND COMMONLY-USED RECORDS.

ROLLER BALLPOINT PEN
BLACK PEN THAT FITS IN FLAP FOR EASY ACCESS.

REFERENCE SECTION
CONTAINS MAPS THAT SHOW AREA CODES AND TIME ZONES, TOLL-FREE NUMBERS FOR TRAVEL ACCOMODATIONS, METRIC CONVERSION CHARTS.

FINANCE SECTION
MULTI-USE LEDGER FORMS, RECEIPT LOG AND STORAGE ENVELOPE, CREDIT CARD INFORMATION.

CALENDAR SECTION
YEARLY, MONTHLY, WEEKLY, AND DAILY ENGAGEMENT CALENDARS SUPPLEMENT THOSE YOU PRINT OUT WITH TRAVELING SIDEKICK.

PENDING SECTION
A "TO BE CONTINUED" SECTION FOR CURRENT PROJECTS, MEETING NOTES, ETC.

CALCULATOR
IN ONE OF TWO BUSINESS-CARD-SIZE STORAGE POCKETS.

TRAVELING SIDEKICK SOFTWARE
GENERATES, UPDATES, AND PRINTS YOUR ADDRESS AND CALENDAR FILES.

What the software program and its Report Generator do for you before you go—and when you get back

Before you go:
- Prints out your calendar, appointments, addresses, phone directory, and whatever other information you need from your data files

When you return:
- Lets you quickly and easily enter all the new names you obtained while you were away into your SideKick data files

It can also:
- Sort your address book by contact, zip code or company name
- Print mailing labels
- Print information selectively
- Search files for existing addresses or calendar engagements

Suggested Retail Price: $69.95 (not copy protected)

Minimum system configuration: IBM PC, XT, AT, Portable, PCjr, 3270 and true compatibles. PC-DOS (MS-DOS) 2.0 or later. 256K RAM mimimum.

 **BORLAND** *INTERNATIONAL*

SUPERKEY:® THE PRODUCTIVITY BOOSTER

RAM-resident
Increased productivity for IBM®PCs or compatibles

SuperKey's simple macros are electronic shortcuts to success. By letting you reduce a lengthy paragraph into a single keystroke of your choice, SuperKey eliminates repetition.

SuperKey turns 1,000 keystrokes into 1!

SuperKey can record lengthy keystroke sequences and play them back at the touch of a single key. Instantly. Like magic.

In fact, with SuperKey's simple macros, you can turn "Dear Customer: Thank you for your inquiry. We are pleased to let you know that shipment will be made within 24 hours. Sincerely," into the one keystroke of your choice!

SuperKey keeps your confidential files—confidential!

Without encryption, your files are open secrets. Anyone can walk up to your PC and read your confidential files (tax returns, business plans, customer lists, personal letters, etc.).

With SuperKey you can encrypt any file, *even* while running another program. As long as you keep the password secret, only *you* can decode your file correctly. SuperKey also implements the U.S. government Data Encryption Standard (DES).

- ☑ RAM resident—accepts new macro files even while running other programs
- ☑ Pull-down menus
- ☑ Superfast file encryption
- ☑ Choice of two encryption schemes
- ☑ On-line context-sensitive help
- ☑ One-finger mode reduces key commands to single keystroke
- ☑ Screen OFF/ON blanks out and restores screen to protect against "burn in"
- ☑ Partial or complete reorganization of keyboard

- ☑ Keyboard buffer increases 16 character keyboard "type-ahead" buffer to 128 characters
- ☑ Real-time delay causes macro playback to pause for specified interval
- ☑ Transparent display macros allow creation of menus on top of application programs
- ☑ Data entry and format control using "fixed" or "variable" fields
- ☑ Command stack recalls last 256 characters entered

Suggested Retail Price: $99.95 (not copy protected)

Minimum system configuration: IBM PC, XT, AT, PCjr, and true compatibles. PC-DOS (MS-DOS) 2.0 or greater. 128K RAM. One disk drive.

BORLAND INTERNATIONAL

SuperKey is a registered trademark of Borland International, Inc. IBM, XT, AT, and PCjr are registered trademarks of International Business Machines Corp. MS-DOS is a registered trademark of Microsoft Corp.

BOR 0062C

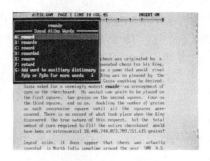

REFLEX.® THE DATABASE MANAGER

The high-performance database manager that's so advanced it's easy to use!

Lets you organize, analyze and report information faster than ever before! If you manage mailing lists, customer files, or even your company's budgets—Reflex is the database manager for you!

Reflex is the acclaimed, high-performance database manager you've been waiting for. Reflex extends database management with business graphics. Because a picture is often worth a 1000 words, Reflex lets you extract critical information buried in mountains of data. With Reflex, when you look, you see.

The **REPORT VIEW** allows you to generate everything from mailing labels to sophisticated reports. You can use database files created with Reflex or transferred from Lotus 1-2-3,® dBASE,® PFS: File,® and other applications.

Reflex: The Critics' Choice

". . . if you use a PC, you should know about Reflex . . . may be the best bargain in software today."
Jerry Pournelle, BYTE

"Everyone agrees that Reflex is the best-looking database they've ever seen."
Adam B. Green, InfoWorld

"The next generation of software has officially arrived."
Peter Norton, PC Week

Reflex: don't use your PC without it!
Join hundreds of thousands of enthusiastic Reflex users and experience the power and ease of use of Borland's award-winning Reflex.

Suggested Retail Price: $149.95 (not copy protected)

Minimum system configuration: IBM PC, XT, AT, and true compatibles. 384K RAM minimum. IBM Color Graphics Adapter, Hercules Monochrome Graphics CArd, or equivalent. PC-DOS (MS-DOS) 2.0 or greater. Hard disk and mouse optional. Lotus 1-2-3, dBASE, or PFS: File optional.

BORLAND
I N T E R N A T I O N A L

REFLEX WORKSHOP™

Includes 22 "instant templates" covering a broad range of business applications (listed below). Also shows you how to customize databases, graphs, crosstabs, and reports. It's an invaluable analytical tool and an important addition to another one of our best sellers, Reflex: The Analyst 1.1.

Fast-start tutorial examples:

Learn Reflex® as you work with practical business applications. The Reflex Workshop Disk supplies databases and reports large enough to illustrate the power and variety of Reflex features. Instructions in each Reflex Workshop chapter take you through a step-by-step analysis of sample data. You then follow simple steps to adapt the files to your own needs.

22 practical business applications:

Workshop's 22 "instant templates" give you a wide range of analytical tools:

Administration
- Scheduling Appointments
- Planning Conference Facilities
- Managing a Project
- Creating a Mailing System
- Managing Employment Applications

Sales and Marketing
- Researching Store Check Inventory
- Tracking Sales Leads
- Summarizing Sales Trends
- Analyzing Trends

Production and Operations
- Summarizing Repair Turnaround

- Tracking Manufacturing Quality Assurance
- Analyzing Product Costs

Accounting and Financial Planning
- Tracking Petty Cash
- Entering Purchase Orders
- Organizing Outgoing Purchase Orders
- Analyzing Accounts Receivable
- Maintaining Letters of Credit
- Reporting Business Expenses
- Managing Debits and Credits
- Examining Leased Inventory Trends
- Tracking Fixed Assets
- Planning Commercial Real Estate Investment

Whether you're a newcomer learning Reflex basics or an experienced "power user" looking for tips, Reflex Workshop will help you quickly become an expert database analyst.

Minimum system configuration: IBM PC, AT, and XT, and true compatibles. PC-DOS (MS-DOS) 2.0 or greater. 384K RAM minimum. Requires Reflex: The Analyst, and IBM Color Graphics Adapter, Hercules Monochrome Graphics Card or equivalent.

BORLAND
INTERNATIONAL

Suggested Retail Price: $69.95 (not copy protected)

TURBO PASCAL
TURBO TUTOR®

VERSION 2.0

Learn Pascal From The Folks Who Created The Turbo Pascal® Family

Borland International proudly presents Turbo Tutor, the perfect complement to your Turbo Pascal compiler. Turbo Tutor is really for everyone— even if you've never programmed before.

And if you're already proficient, Turbo Tutor can sharpen up the fine points. The manual and program disk focus on the whole spectrum of Turbo Pascal programming techniques.

- **For the Novice:** It gives you a concise history of Pascal, tells you how to write a simple program, and defines the basic programming terms you need to know.

- **Programmer's Guide:** The heart of Turbo Pascal. The manual covers the fine points of every aspect of Turbo Pascal programming: program structure, data types, control structures, procedures and functions, scalar types, arrays, strings, pointers, sets, files, and records.

- **Advanced Concepts:** If you're an expert, you'll love the sections detailing such topics as linked lists, trees, and graphs. You'll also find sample program examples for PC-DOS and MS-DOS.®

10,000 lines of commented source code, demonstrations of 20 Turbo Pascal features, multiple-choice quizzes, an interactive on-line tutor, and more!

Turbo Tutor may be the only reference work about Pascal and programming you'll ever need!

Suggested Retail Price: $39.95 (not copy protected)

Minimum system configuration: Turbo Pascal 3.0. PC-DOS (MS-DOS) 2.0 or later. 192K RAM minimum (CP/M-80 version 2.2 or later: 64K RAM minimum).

 **BORLAND** *INTERNATIONAL*

TURBO PASCAL
GRAPHIX TOOLBOX®

A Library of Graphics Routines for Use with Turbo Pascal®

High-resolution graphics for your IBM˚ PC, AT,˚ XT,˚ PCjr˚, true PC compatibles, and the Heath Zenith Z-100.˚ Comes complete with graphics window management.

Even if you're new to Turbo Pascal programming, the Turbo Pascal Graphix Toolbox will get you started right away. It's a collection of tools that will get you right into the fascinating world of high-resolution business graphics, including graphics window management. You get immediate, satisfying results. And we keep Royalty out of American business because you don't pay any—even if you distribute your own compiled programs that include all or part of the Turbo Pascal Graphix Toolbox procedures.

What you get includes:

- Complete commented source code on disk.
- Tools for drawing simple graphics.
- Tools for drawing complex graphics, including curves with optional smoothing.
- Routines that let you store and restore graphic images to and from disk.
- Tools allowing you to send screen images to Epson®-compatible printers.

- Full graphics window management.
- Two different font styles for graphic labeling.
- Choice of line-drawing styles.
- Routines that will let you quickly plot functions and model experimental data.
- And much, much more . . .

"While most people only talk about low-cost personal computer software, Borland has been doing something about it. And Borland provides good technical support as part of the price."
John Markov & Paul Freiberger, syndicated columnists.

If you ever plan to create Turbo Pascal programs that make use of business graphics or scientific graphics, you need the Turbo Pascal Graphix Toolbox.

Suggested Retail Price: $69.95 (not copy protected)

Minimum system configuration: IBM PC, XT, AT, PCjr, true compatibles and the Heath Zenith Z-100. Turbo Pascal 3.0 or later. 192K RAM minimum. Two disk drives and an IBM Color Graphics Adapter (CGA), IBM Enhanced Graphics Adapter (EGA), Hercules Graphics Card or compatible.

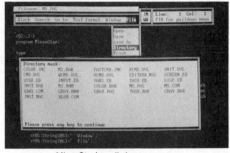

TURBO PASCAL GAMEWORKS®

Secrets And Strategies Of The Masters Are Revealed For The First Time

Explore the world of state-of-the-art computer games with Turbo GameWorks. Using easy-to-understand examples, Turbo GameWorks teaches you techniques to quickly create your own computer games using Turbo Pascal.® Or, for instant excitement, play the three great computer games we've included on disk—compiled and ready to run.

TURBO CHESS

Test your chess-playing skills against your computer challenger. With Turbo GameWorks, you're on your way to becoming a master chess player. Explore the complete Turbo Pascal source code and discover the secrets of Turbo Chess.

"What impressed me the most was the fact that with this program you can become a computer chess analyst. You can add new variations to the program at any time and make the program play stronger and stronger chess. There's no limit to the fun and enjoyment of playing Turbo GameWorks Chess, and most important of all, with this chess program there's no limit to how it can help you improve your game."

—George Koltanowski, Dean of American Chess, former President of the United Chess Federation, and syndicated chess columnist.

TURBO BRIDGE

Now play the world's most popular card game—bridge. Play one-on-one with your computer or against up to three other opponents. With Turbo Pascal source code, you can even program your own bidding or scoring conventions.

"There has never been a bridge program written which plays at the expert level, and the ambitious user will enjoy tackling that challenge, with the format already structured in the program. And for the inexperienced player, the bridge program provides an easy-to-follow format that allows the user to start right out playing. The user can 'play bridge' against real competition without having to gather three other people."

—Kit Woolsey, writer of several articles and books on bridge, and twice champion of the Blue Ribbon Pairs.

TURBO GO-MOKU

Prepare for battle when you challenge your computer to a game of Go-Moku—the exciting strategy game also known as Pente.® In this battle of wits, you and the computer take turns placing X's and O's on a grid of 19×19 squares until five pieces are lined up in a row. Vary the game if you like, using the source code available on your disk.

Suggested Retail Price: $69.95 (not copy protected)

Minimum system configuration: IBM PC, XT, AT, Portable, 3270, PCjr, and true compatibles. PC-DOS (MS-DOS) 2.0 or later. 192K RAM minimum. To edit and compile the Turbo Pascal source code, you must be using Turbo Pascal 3.0 for IBM PCs and compatibles.

Turbo Pascal and Turbo GameWorks are registered trademarks of Borland International, Inc. Pente is a registered trademark of Parker Brothers. IBM, XT, AT, and PCjr are registered trademarks of International Business Machines Corporation. MS-DOS is a registered trademark of Microsoft Corporation. Copyright 1987 Borland International

BOR0065C

TURBO PROLOG™

the natural language of Artificial Intelligence

Turbo Prolog brings fifth-generation supercomputer power to your IBM®PC!

Turbo Prolog takes programming into a new, natural, and logical environment

With Turbo Prolog, because of its natural, logical approach, both people new to programming *and* professional programmers can build powerful applications such as expert systems, customized knowledge bases, natural language interfaces, and smart information management systems.

Turbo Prolog is a *declarative* language which uses deductive reasoning to solve programming problems.

Turbo Prolog provides a fully integrated programming environment like Borland's Turbo Pascal,® the *de facto* worldwide standard.

You get the complete Turbo Prolog programming system

You get the 200-page manual you're holding, software that includes the lightning-fast Turbo Prolog six-pass compiler and interactive editor, and the free GeoBase natural query language database, which includes commented source code on disk, ready to compile. (GeoBase is a complete database designed and developed around U.S. geography. You can modify it or use it "as is.")

Turbo Prolog's development system includes:

- ☐ A complete Prolog compiler that is a variation of the Clocksin and Mellish Edinburgh standard Prolog.
- ☐ A full-screen interactive editor.
- ☐ Support for both graphic and text windows.
- ☐ All the tools that let you build your own expert systems and **AI** applications with unprecedented ease.

Minimum system configuration: IBM PC, XT, AT, Portable, 3270, PCjr and true compatibles. PC-DOS (MS-DOS) 2.0 or later. 384K RAM minimum.

Suggested Retail Price: $99.95 (not copy protected)

BORLAND
INTERNATIONAL

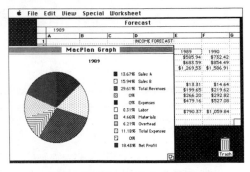

REFLEX: THE DATABASE MANAGER

The easy-to-use relational database that thinks like a spreadsheet. Reflex for the Mac lets you crunch numbers by entering formulas and link databases by drawing on-screen lines.

5 free ready-to-use templates are included on the examples disk:

- A sample 1040 tax application with Schedule A, Schedule B, and Schedule D, each contained in a separate report document.
- A portfolio analysis application with linked databases of stock purchases, sales, and dividend payments.
- A checkbook application.

- A client billing application set up for a law office, but easily customized by any professional who bills time.
- A parts explosion application that breaks down an object into its component parts for cost analysis.

Reflex for the Mac accomplishes all of these tasks without programming—using spreadsheet-like formulas. Some other Reflex for the Mac features are:

- Visual database design.
- "What you see is what you get" report and form layout with pictures.
- Automatic restructuring of database files when data types are changed, or fields are added and deleted.
- Display formats which include General, Decimal, Scientific, Dollars, Percent.

- Data types which include variable length text, number, integer, automatically incremented sequence number, date, time, and logical.
- Up to 255 fields per record.
- Up to 16 files simultaneously open.
- Up to 16 Mac fonts and styles are selectable for individual fields and labels.

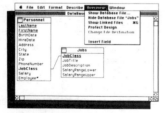

After opening the "Overview" window, you draw link lines between databases directly onto your Macintosh screen.

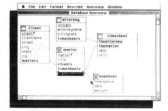

The link lines you draw establish both visual and electronic relationships between your databases.

You can have multiple windows open simultaneously to view all members of a linked set—which are interactive and truly relational.

Critic's Choice

". . . a powerful relational database . . . uses a visual approach to information management." **InfoWorld**

". . . gives you a lot of freedom in report design; you can even import graphics." **A+ Magazine**

". . . bridges the gap between the pretty programs and the power programs." **Stewart Alsop, PC Letter**

BORLAND
INTERNATIONAL

Suggested Retail Price: $99.95*
(not copy protected)

Minimum system configuration: Macintosh 512K or Macintosh Plus with one disk drive. Second external drive recommended.

Reflex is a registered trademark of Borland/Analytica, Inc. Macintosh is a trademark of McIntosh Laboratory, Inc. and is used with express permission of its owner.
Copyright 1987 Borland International

BOR0149A

TURBO PASCAL® MACINTOSH™

The ultimate Pascal development environment

Borland's new Turbo Pascal for the Mac is so incredibly fast that it can compile 1,420 lines of source code in the 7.1 seconds it took you to read this!

And reading the rest of this takes about *5 minutes*, which is plenty of time for Turbo Pascal for the Mac to compile at least *60,000 more lines* of source code!

Turbo Pascal for the Mac does both Windows and "Units"
The *separate* compilation of routines offered by Turbo Pascal for the Mac creates modules called "Units," which can be linked to any Turbo Pascal program. This "modular pathway" gives you "pieces" which can then be integrated into larger programs. You get a more efficient use of memory and a reduction in the time it takes to develop large programs.

Turbo Pascal for the Mac is so compatible with Lisa® that they should be living together
Routines from Macintosh Programmer's Workshop Pascal and Inside Macintosh can be compiled and run with only the subtlest changes. Turbo Pascal for the Mac is also compatible with the Hierarchical File System of the Macintosh.

The 27-second Guide to Turbo Pascal for the Mac

- Compilation speed of more than 12,000 lines per minute
- "Unit" structure lets you create programs in modular form
- Multiple editing windows—up to 8 at once
- Compilation options include compiling to disk or memory, or compile and run
- No need to switch between programs to compile or run a program
- Streamlined development and debugging
- Compatibility with Macintosh Programmer's
- Workshop Pascal (with minimal changes)
- Compatibility with Hierarchical File System of your Mac
- Ability to define default volume and folder names used in compiler directives
- Search and change features in the editor speed up and simplify alteration of routines
- Ability to use all available Macintosh memory without limit
- "Units" included to call all the routines provided by Macintosh Toolbox

---

Suggested Retail Price: $99.95* (not copy protected)

Minimum system configuration: Macintosh 512K or Macintosh Plus with one disk drive.

Turbo Pascal and SideKick are registered trademarks of Borland International, Inc. and Reflex is a registered trademark of Borland/Analytica, Inc. Macintosh is a trademark of McIntosh Laboratories, Inc. licensed to Apple Computer with its express permission. Lisa is a registered trademark of Apple Computer, Inc. Inside Macintosh is a copyright of Apple Computer, Inc.
Copyright 1987 Borland International BOR 0167A

TURBO PASCAL® TUTOR

From the folks who created Turbo Pascal. Borland's new Turbo Pascal Tutor is everything you need to start programming in Turbo Pascal on the Macintosh!™ It takes you from the bare basics to advanced programming in a simple, easy-to-understand fashion.

No gimmicks. It's all here.

The manual, the Tutor application, and 30 sample programs provide a step-by-step tutorial in three phases: programming in Pascal, programming on the Macintosh, and programming in Turbo Pascal on the Macintosh. Here's how the manual is set up:

Turbo Pascal for the Absolute Novice
delivers the basics—a concise history of Pascal, key terminology, your first program.

A Programmer's Guide to Turbo Pascal
covers Pascal specifics—program structure, procedures and functions, arrays, strings, and so on. We've also included Turbo Typist, a textbook sample program.

Advanced Programming
takes you a step higher into stacks, queues, binary trees, linked structures, writing large programs, and more.

Using the Power of the Macintosh
discusses the revolutionary hardware and software features of this machine. It introduces the 600-plus utility routines in the Apple Toolbox.

Programming the Macintosh in Turbo Pascal
shows you how to create true Macintosh programs that use graphics, pull-down menus, dialog boxes, and so on. Finally, MacTypist, a complete stand-alone application featuring animated graphics, builds on Turbo Typist and demonstrates what you can do with all the knowledge you've just acquired.

The disk contains the source code for all the sample programs, including Turbo Typist, MacTypist, and Turbo Tutor. The Tutor's split screen lets you run a procedure and view its source code simultaneously. After running it, you can take a test on the procedure. If you're stuck for an answer, a Hint option steers you in the right direction.

Macintosh topics included are

- ☑ memory management
- ☑ resources and resource files
- ☑ QuickDraw
- ☑ events
- ☑ windows
- ☑ controls
- ☑ menus
- ☑ desk accessory support
- ☑ dialogs
- ☑ File Manager
- ☑ debugging

Suggested Retail Price: $69.95

Minimum system requirements: Any Macintosh with at least 512K of RAM. Requires Turbo Pascal.

BORLAND
I N T E R N A T I O N A L

TURBO C®

A complete interactive development environment

With Turbo C, you can expect what only Borland delivers: Quality, Speed, Power and Price. And with its compilation speed of more than 7000 lines a minute, Turbo C makes everything else look like an exercise in slow motion.

Turbo C: The C compiler for both amateurs and professionals

If you're just beginning and you've "kinda wanted to learn C," now's your chance to do it the easy way. Turbo C's got everything to get you going. If you're already programming in C, switching to Turbo C will considerably increase your productivity and help make your programs both smaller and faster.

Turbo C: a complete interactive development environment

Like Turbo Pascal® and Turbo Prolog,™ Turbo C comes with an interactive editor that will show you syntax errors right in your source code. Developing, debugging, and running a Turbo C program is a snap!

Technical Specifications

☑ Compiler: One-pass compiler generating native in-line code, linkable object modules and assembler. The object module format is compatible with the PC-DOS linker. Supports small, medium, compact, large, and huge memory model libraries. Can mix models with near and far pointers. Includes floating point emulator (utilizes 8087/80287 if installed).

☑ Interactive Editor: The system includes a powerful, interactive full-screen text editor. If the compiler detects an error, the editor automatically positions the cursor appropriately in the source code.

☑ Development Environment: A powerful "Make" is included so that managing Turbo C program development is easy. Borland's fast "Turbo Linker" is also included. Also includes pull-down menus and windows. Can run from the environment or generate an executable file.

☑ Links with relocatable object modules created using Borland's Turbo Prolog into a single program.

☑ ANSI C compatible.

☑ Start-up routine source code included.

☑ Both command line and integrated environment versions included.

"Sieve" benchmark (25 iterations)

	Turbo C	Microsoft® C	Lattice C
Compile time	**3.89**	16.37	13.90
Compile and link time	**9.94**	29.06	27.79
Execution time	**5.77**	9.51	13.79
Object code size	**274**	297	301
Price	**$99.95**	$450.00	$500.00

Benchmark run on a 6 Mhz IBM AT using Turbo C version 1.0 and the Turbo Linker version 1.0; Microsoft C version 4.0 and the MS overlay linker version 3.51; Lattice C version 3.1 and the MS object linker version 3.05.

Suggested Retail Price: $99.95* (not copy protected)

Minimum system configuration: IBM PC, XT, AT and true compatibles. PC-DOS (MS-DOS) 2.0 or later. One floppy drive. 320K.

Turbo C and Turbo Pascal are registered trademarks and Turbo Prolog is a trademark of Borland International, Inc. Microsoft C and MS-DOS are registered trademarks of Microsoft Corp. Lattice C is a registered trademark of Lattice, Inc. IBM, XT, and AT are registered trademarks of International Business Machines Corp.

BOR 0243

Borland
Software

For the dealer nearest you
or to order by phone
Call (800) 543-7543

BORLAND
I N T E R N A T I O N A L

4585 Scotts Valley Drive
Scotts Valley, CA 95066

Index

NOTES

NOTES

NOTES

NOTES